Glencoe Mathematics

Pre-Algebra

Chapter 13
Resource Masters

New York, New York   Columbus, Ohio   Chicago, Illinois   Peoria, Illinois   Woodland Hills, California

Consumable Workbooks Many of the worksheets contained in the Chapter Resource Masters are available as consumable workbooks in both English and Spanish.

	ISBN10	ISBN13
Study Guide and Intervention Workbook	0-07-877224-1	978-0-07-877224-6
Skills Practice Workbook	0-07-877216-8	978-0-07-877216-0
Practice Workbook	0-07-877218-4	978-0-07-877218-4
Word Problem Practice Workbook	0-07-877220-6	978-0-07-877220-7

Spanish Versions

Study Guide and Intervention Workbook	0-07-877224-1	978-0-07-877224-6
Skills Practice Workbook	0-07-877217-6	978-0-07-877217-7
Practice Workbook	0-07-877219-2	978-0-07-877219-1
Word Problem Practice Workbook	0-07-877221-4	978-0-07-877221-4

Answers for Workbooks The answers for Chapter 13 of these workbooks can be found in the back of this Chapter Resource Masters booklet.

StudentWorks Plus™ This CD-ROM includes the entire Student Edition test along with the English workbooks listed above.

TeacherWorks Plus™ All of the materials found in this booklet are included for viewing, printing, and editing in this CD-ROM.

Spanish Assessment Masters (ISBN10: 0-07-877222-2, ISBN13: 978-0-07-877222-1) These masters contain a Spanish version of Chapter 13 Test Form 2A and Form 2C.

 **Glencoe**

The *McGraw-Hill* Companies

Send all inquiries to:
Glencoe/McGraw-Hill
8787 Orion Place
Columbus, OH 43240

ISBN13: 978-0-07-873943-9
ISBN10: 0-07-873943-8

Printed in the United States of America.

2 3 4 5 6 7 8 9 10 024 13 12 11 10 09 08 07

Contents

Teacher's Guide to Using the Chapter 13 Resource Masters

The *Chapter 13 Resource Masters* includes the core materials needed for Chapter 13. These materials include worksheets, extensions, and assessment options. The answers for these pages appear at the back of this booklet.

All of the materials found in this booklet are included for viewing and printing in the *TeacherWorks Plus*[TM] CD-ROM.

Chapter Resources

Student-Built Glossary (pages 1–2) These masters are a student study tool that presents up to twenty of the key vocabulary terms from the chapter. Students are to record definitions and/or examples for each term. You may suggest that students highlight or star the terms with which they are not familiar. Give this to students before beginning Lesson 13-1. Encourage them to add these pages to their mathematics study notebooks. Remind them to complete the appropriate words as they study each lesson.

Anticipation Guide (pages 3–4) This master, presented in both English and Spanish, is a survey used before beginning the chapter to pinpoint what students may or may not know about the concepts in the chapter. Students will revisit this survey after they complete the chapter to see if their perceptions have changed.

Lesson Resources

Lesson Reading Guide Get Ready for the Lesson extends the discussion from the beginning of the Student Edition lesson. Read the Lesson asks students to interpret the context of and relationships among terms in the lesson. Finally, Remember What You Learned asks students to summarize what they have learned using various representation techniques. Use as a study tool for note taking or as an informal reading assignment. It is also a helpful tool for ELL (English Language Learners).

Study Guide and Intervention This master provides vocabulary, key concepts, additional worked-out examples and Check Your Progress exercises to use as a reteaching activity. It can also be used in conjunction with the Student Edition as an instructional tool for students who have been absent.

Skills Practice This master focuses more on the computational nature of the lesson. Use as an additional practice option or as homework for second-day teaching of the lesson.

Practice This master closely follows the types of problems found in the Exercises section of the Student Edition and includes word problems. Use as an additional practice option or as homework for second-day teaching of the lesson.

Word Problem Practice This master includes additional practice in solving word problems that apply the concepts of the lesson. Use as an additional practice or as homework for second-day teaching of the lesson.

Enrichment These activities may extend the concepts of the lesson, offer a historical or multicultural look at the concepts, or widen students' perspectives on the mathematics they are learning. They are written for use with all levels of students.

Graphing Calculator, Scientific Calculator, or Spreadsheet Activities

These activities present ways in which technology can be used with the concepts in some lessons of this chapter. Use as an alternative approach to some concepts or as an integral part of your lesson presentation.

Assessment Options

The assessment masters in the *Chapter 13 Resource Masters* offer a wide range of assessment tools for formative (monitoring) assessment and summative (final) assessment.

Student Recording Sheet This master corresponds with the standardized test practice at the end of the chapter.

Pre-AP Rubric This master provides information for teachers and students on how to assess performance on open-ended questions.

Quizzes Four free-response quizzes offer assessment at appropriate intervals in the chapter.

Mid-Chapter Test This 1-page test provides an option to assess the first half of the chapter. It parallels the timing of the Mid-Chapter Quiz in the Student Edition and includes both multiple-choice and free-response questions.

Vocabulary Test This test is suitable for all students. It includes a list of vocabulary words and 10 questions to assess students' knowledge of those words. This can also be used in conjunction with one of the leveled chapter tests.

Leveled Chapter Tests

- *Form 1* contains multiple-choice questions and is intended for use with below grade level students.
- *Forms 2A and 2B* contain multiple-choice questions aimed at on grade level students. These tests are similar in format to offer comparable testing situations.
- *Forms 2C and 2D* contain free-response questions aimed at on grade level students. These tests are similar in format to offer comparable testing situations.
- *Form 3* is a free-response test for use with above grade level students.

All of the above tests include a free-response Bonus question.

Extended-Response Test Performance assessment tasks are suitable for all students. Sample answers and a scoring rubric are included for evaluation.

Standardized Test Practice These three pages are cumulative in nature. It includes three parts: multiple-choice questions with bubble-in answer format, griddable questions with answer grids, and short-answer free-response questions.

Answers

- The answers for the Anticipation Guide and Lesson Resources are provided as reduced pages with answers appearing in red.
- Full-size answer keys are provided for the assessment masters.

13   **Student-Built Glossary**

This is an alphabetical list of key vocabulary terms you will learn in Chapter 13. As you study this chapter, complete each term's definition or description. Remember to add the page number where you found the term. Add these pages to your Pre-Algebra Study Notebook to review vocabulary at the end of the chapter.

Vocabulary Term	Found on Page	Definition/Description/Example
binomial by-NOH-mee-uhl		
cubic function KYOO-bihk		
degree		

13 Student-Built Glossary *(continued)*

Vocabulary Term	Found on Page	Definition/Description/Example
nonlinear function		
polynomial PAHL-uh-NOH-mee-uhl		
quadratic function kwah-DRAT-ihk		
trinomial try-NOH-mee-uhl		

13 Anticipation Guide

Equations

Step 1 ▸ *Before you begin Chapter 13*

- Read each statement.

- Decide whether you Agree (A) or Disagree (D) with the statement.

- Write A or D in the first column OR if you are not sure whether you agree or disagree, write NS (Not Sure).

STEP 1 A, D, or NS	Statement	Step 2 A or D
	1. A trinomial is a polynomial with three terms.	
	2. All polynomials are also binomials.	
	3. The expression $x^2 + \dfrac{1}{x}$ is not a polynomial because it has a variable in the denominator.	
	4. The degree of a polynomial is found by counting the number of terms.	
	5. $8a$ and $7c$ are called like terms because both contain variables to the first power.	
	6. To add two polynomials, add all like terms together.	
	7. $-1(3x + 4)$ is equivalent to $-3 + 4$.	
	8. In the expression $4t(2t^2 - 5)$, the Distributive Property can not be used because the variable t is raised to two different powers.	
	9. A function whose graph is a curve is a nonlinear function.	
	10. To graph the function $y = 6x^2$, make a table of values, plot the ordered pairs, and connect the points with a curve.	

Step 2 ▸ *After you complete Chapter 13*

- Reread each statement and complete the last column by entering an A (Agree) or a D (Disagree).

- Did any of your opinions about the statements change from the first column?

- For those statements that you mark with a D, use a separate sheet of paper to explain why you disagree. Use examples, if possible.

13 Ejercicios preparatorios

Funciones polinomiales y no lineales

Paso 1 — *Antes de comenzar el Capítulo 13*

- Lee cada enunciado.
- Decide si estás de acuerdo (A) o en desacuerdo (D) con el enunciado.
- Escribe A o D en la primera columna O si no estás seguro(a) de la respuesta, escribe NS (No estoy seguro(a)).

PASO 1 A, D o NS	Enunciado	PASO 2 A o D
	1. Un trinomio es un polinomio con tres términos.	
	2. Todos los polinomios son también binomios.	
	3. La expresión $x^2 + \dfrac{1}{x}$ x no es un polinomio porque tiene una variable en el denominador.	
	4. El grado de un polinomio se encuentra al contar el número de términos.	
	5. $8a$ y $7c$ se llaman términos semejantes porque ambos contienen variables elevadas a la primera potencia.	
	6. Para sumar dos polinomios, suma juntos todos los términos semejantes.	
	7. $-1(3x + 4)$ es equivalente a $-3 + 4$.	
	8. En la expresión $4t(2t^2 - 5)$, no se puede usar la propiedad distributiva porque la variable t está elevada a dos potencias diferentes.	
	9. Una función cuya gráfica es una curva es una función no lineal.	
	10. Para graficar la función $y = 6x^2$, haz una tabla de valores, diagrama los pares ordenados y conecta los puntos con una curva.	

Paso 2 — *Después de completar el Capítulo 13*

- Vuelve a leer cada enunciado y completa la última columna con una A o una D.
- ¿Cambió cualquiera de tus opiniones sobre los enunciados de la primera columna?
- En una hoja de papel aparte, escribe un ejemplo de por qué estás en desacuerdo con los enunciados que marcaste con una D.

13-1 Lesson Reading Guide

Polynomials

Get Ready for the Lesson

Read the introduction to Lesson 13-1 in your textbook. Write your answers below.

a. How many terms are in the expression for the heat index?

b. What separates the terms of the expression?

Read the Lesson

Write a definition and give an example of each new vocabulary phrase.

Vocabulary	Definition	Example
1. polynomial		
2. binomial		
3. trinomial		
4. degree		

Remember What You Learned

5. Notice that the words *binomial, trinomial,* and *polynomial* contain the same root—*nomial,* but have different prefixes.

   a. Find the definition of the prefix *bi-* in a dictionary. Write the definition. Explain how it can help you remember the meaning of *binomial.*

   b. Find the definition of the prefix *tri-* in a dictionary. Write the definition. Explain how it can help you remember the meaning of *trinomial.*

   c. Find the definition of the prefix *poly-* in a dictionary. Write the definition. Explain how it can help you remember the meaning of *polynomial.*

13-1 Study Guide and Intervention
Polynomials

Classify Polynomials Polynomials are classified according to the number of terms they have. A *monomial* has one term, a *binomial* has two terms, and a *trinomial* has three terms. The exponent of a variable in a monomial must be a whole number, and the variable cannot be in the denominator or under a radical sign.

Example 1 Determine whether each expression is a polynomial. If it is, classify it as a *monomial, binomial,* or *trinomial.*

a. $2y + \dfrac{3}{y}$

The expression is not a polynomial because $\dfrac{3}{y}$ has a variable in the denominator.

b. $\dfrac{3a}{4} + 6a^3 - 5a^4$

The expression is a polynomial with three terms, so it is a trinomial.

Degree of Polynomials A polynomial also has a degree. The degree of a polynomial is the same as that of the term with the greatest degree. The degree of a term is the sum of the exponents of its variables.

Example 2 Find the degree of each polynomial.

a. $x^6 - 3x^4 + 1$

The greatest degree is 6, so the degree of the trinomial is 6.

b. $10b^2c + 8bc - c^2$

$10b^2c$ has degree $2 + 1$ or 3. $8bc$ has degree $1 + 1$ or 2. c^2 has degree 2. The greatest degree is 3, so the trinomial has degree 3.

Exercises

Determine whether each expression is a polynomial. If it is, classify it as a *monomial, binomial,* or *trinomial.*

1. $7q + r - 10$

2. $\sqrt{8r}$

3. $x^2 - 4$

4. -89

5. $3v^2 + 4w$

6. $a^5 + b^2 + c$

Find the degree of each polynomial.

7. $28y$

8. $-5h$

9. $2x^3y$

10. $9p^3 - 6p^2$

11. $mn^5 + mn^4 + m^2$

12. $8x^2 + 4xy - y^2$

13-1 Skills Practice

Polynomials

Determine whether each expression is a polynomial. If it is, classify it as a *monomial*, *binomial*, or *trinomial*.

1. $-5g^8$

2. $x + 2y + z$

3. $5x + 1 + \dfrac{4}{x}$

4. $r^2 - 9r$

5. $d + 1$

6. $a^3b^2 + a^2$

7. n

8. $17 - \sqrt{c}$

9. $a + b^2 - 3$

10. $m + 2\sqrt{m}$

11. $5y^2 - 3y + 1$

12. $a - b + c$

13. $24x^3$

14. $25 - 9h^4$

15. $u^5 + u^3 + u$

16. $\dfrac{3x^3}{4} + \dfrac{x}{2} + \dfrac{1}{8}$

17. $\dfrac{x}{5} + \dfrac{1}{2}$

18. $\dfrac{6}{a^2} - \dfrac{1}{a} + \dfrac{1}{3}$

19. 1

20. $9y - \sqrt{5}$

21. $27g^5h^2$

Find the degree of each polynomial.

22. 14

23. ab

24. b

25. $c^3 + c^2 + c + 1$

26. mn^5

27. $xy^3z + 1$

28. $k - 4$

29. $\dfrac{-5}{6}$

30. 9.7

31. $c^6de^3 + c^5 + d$

32. $a^2 - 2a + 3$

33. $k^3 + 3k^4$

34. $xy^2 + 4x^2y + y^2$

35. $7b^5 - 10$

36. $16g + 3$

37. $8y^2 + 8y - 5$

38. $abc + 2ab + 5c - bc + 1$

39. $-4g^2h^5 + 2gh^4 + 9$

13-1 Practice

Polynomials

Determine whether each expression is a polynomial. If it is, classify it as a monomial, binomial, or trinomial.

1. $-3n^2$

2. $v^2 - 9v$

3. $g + 2h + jk$

4. $6b + 2 + \dfrac{8}{b}$

5. $m + 10$

6. $a^2b^2 + 9$

7. $1 + \sqrt{s}$

8. q

9. $h + h^2 + 1$

10. $m + n - p$

11. $y^4 + 5y - 2$

12. $x - \sqrt{x}$

13. $-5w^7t$

14. $41 - qr^4$

15. $p^4 + p^2 + p$

16. $\dfrac{2x^2}{7} + \dfrac{5x}{7} + \dfrac{3}{7}$

17. $\dfrac{v}{5} + \dfrac{1}{2}$

18. $10k - \sqrt{6}$

19. 4

20. $\dfrac{3}{c^2} - \dfrac{5}{c} - \dfrac{1}{2}$

21. $7g^2h^7$

Find the degree of each polynomial.

22. -52

23. xy

24. c

25. $2c^5 - c^3 - c - 9$

26. ab^3

27. $2xy^4z^3 + 7$

28. $r - 25$

29. $\dfrac{-4}{9}$

30. 12.4

31. $12 + 9t - t^2$

32. $5a^3 - a + 8$

33. $1 - c^2 + c^4$

34. $xy^2 - 3x^2y + xy$

35. $b^5 + b - 1.5$

36. $15k + 2$

37. $cde^8 + c^4 + 2e$

38. $wxyz - 2wx - 5y - yz + 4$

39. $-6g^2h^8 + gh^5 + 3$

40. METEOROLOGY *Summer simmer index* measures the discomfort level due to temperature and humidity. Meteorologists calculate this value by using a polynomial similar to $1.98x^2 - 115.93x + 0.01xy - 0.63y + 6.33$. The variable x is the temperature in °F and y is the relative humidity expressed as a whole number. What is the degree of the polynomial?

13-1 Word Problem Practice

Polynomials

1. **PLANETS** The diameter of a planet can be found by knowing the distance from the viewer to the planet, d, and the planet's angular size, A, or how big it appears to be. The approximate diameter is found using the expression $\frac{2\pi}{360} dA$. Is this expression a polynomial? Explain. If it is, classify it as *monomial*, *binomial*, or *trinomial*.

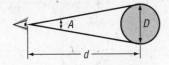

2. **AIRPLANES** The steady ascent of an airplane is represented by the equation $y = \frac{3}{7}x + 2$. What is the degree of the polynomial?

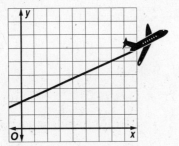

3. **BASKETBALL** A basketball player takes a shot from inside the foul line. The ball travels on an arch according to the equation $y = -0.6x^2 + 3.2x + 6$. Classify the equation as *monomial*, *binomial*, or *trinomial* and find the degree of the polynomial.

4. **DIVING** A diver practices for an upcoming meet. She dives from a platform and follows a trajectory that can be expressed by the equation $y = 2x^4 + 12x$. Classify the equation as *monomial*, *binomial*, or *trinomial* and find the degree of the polynomial.

ROCK CLIMBING For Exercises 5–7, use the following information.

A rock climber plans to climb up one side of the mountain and down the other.

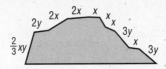

5. Write the polynomial expression that represents the distance the rock climber will travel.

6. Classify the polynomial as a *monomial*, *binomial*, or *trinomial*.

7. What is the degree of the polynomial?

13-1 Enrichment

A Cross-Number Puzzle

Use the clues at the bottom of the page to complete the puzzle. Write one digit in each box.

Across

A $x^2 - 4$ for $x = 5$

B $3xy^2$ for $x = 4$ and $y = -1$

C $(2x + 50) + (x - 15)$ for $x = 0$

E $x^2 - 4x - y^2$ for $x = 10$ and $y = 5$

G $x^2 y$ for $x = 3$ and $y = 7$

I $10w + 5y$ for $w = 6$ and $y = 1$

K $3x^2 + 5x + 8$ for $x = -10$

L $(y - 8) + (10 - 4y)$ for $y = -6$

M $23x - 16x$ for $x = 11$

O $7x + 100y$ for $x = 5$ and $y = 6$

Q $(6x^2 - 2) + (4x^2 - 3)$ for $x = -7$

T $(x^2 - x + 7) + (x^2 - 2)$ for $x = 3$

U $x^2 y$ for $x = -2$ and $y = 8$

V $7y - 12y - 2$ for $y = -10$

W $w^2 - w - 7$ for $w = 9$

Down

A $(6x^2 - 1) + (4x^2 - 3)$ for $x = 5$

B $7y + 8y - 2$ for $y = 1$

D $x + x^2 y^2$ for $x = 7$ and $y = 1$

F $5(7w + 3w)$ for $w = 10$

H $(z^2 + 2z + 1) + (z^2 - 2z - 2)$ for $z = 4$

J $6xy^2 - xy + 60$ for $x = 10$ and $y = 10$

K $w^2 - w - 3$ for $w = 6$

L $(3y - 20) + (45 - 3y)$ for $y = 16$

M $11x^2 - 8x^2$ for $x = -5$

N $x^2 - 2x + y^2$ for $x = 10$ and $y = 8$

P $(2x + 52) + (x - 11)$ for $x = -3$

R $2x^2 - 5x - 140$ for $x = 12$

S $(y - 75) + (120 + 4y)$ for $y = -6$

13-2 Lesson Reading Guide

Adding Polynomials

Get Ready for the Lesson

Read the introduction to Lesson 13-2 in your textbook. Write your answers below.

a. Write the polynomial for the tiles that remain.

b. Find the sum of $x^2 + 4x + 2$ and $7x^2 - 2x + 3$ by using algebra tiles.

c. Compare and contrast finding the sums of polynomials with finding the sum of integers.

Read the Lesson

1. Draw a model that shows $(x^2 - 4x + 2) + (2x^2 + 2x - 3)$. Write the polynomial that shows the sum.

2. Show how to find the sum $(5x - 2) + (4x + 4)$ both vertically and horizontally.

    Vertically   **Horizontally**

Remember What You Learned

3. You have learned that you can combine like terms. On the left below, write three pairs of monomials that have like terms. On the right below, write three pairs of monomials that have unlike terms. Explain your answers.

    Like Terms   **Unlike Terms**

      1.   1.

      2.   2.

      3.   3.

Lesson 13-2

13-2 **Study Guide and Intervention**

Adding Polynomials

Add Polynomials Add polynomials by combining like terms, which are monomials that contain the same variables to the same power.

Example Find $(8x^2 - 7x + 1) + (x^2 + 5)$.

Method 1 Add vertically.

$$
\begin{array}{r}
8x^2 - 7x + 1 \\
(+)\ x^2 \qquad + 5 \\
\hline
9x^2 - 7x + 6
\end{array}
$$

Method 2 Add horizontally.

$(8x^2 - 7x + 1) + (x^2 + 5)$
$= (8x^2 + x^2) - 7x + (1 + 5)$
$= 9x^2 - 7x + 6$

Exercises

Find each sum.

1.
$$
\begin{array}{r}
3x - 7 \\
(+)\ x + 1 \\
\hline
\end{array}
$$

2.
$$
\begin{array}{r}
6d + 8 \\
(+)\ -4d + 1 \\
\hline
\end{array}
$$

3.
$$
\begin{array}{r}
4w^2 - 6w + 3 \\
(+)\ w^2 \qquad - 5 \\
\hline
\end{array}
$$

4.
$$
\begin{array}{r}
5a^2 - a \\
(+) \qquad 2a - 5 \\
\hline
\end{array}
$$

5. $(-m + 3) + (7m - 1)$

6. $(9x^2 + 3x - 1) + (4x + 1)$

7. $(2k^2 - k) + (k - 1)$

8. $(5a^2 + 6ab) + (-ab + b^2)$

9. $(4c^2 - 7) + (c^2 - 3c + 6)$

10. $(x^2 + y) + (xy + y)$

11. $(12h - 6) + (h^2 - 8h + 6)$

12. $(10x^2 + x + 5) + (x - 10x^2)$

13. $(6y^2 - y + 1) + (y^2 - 3y - 6)$

14. $(p^3 + 4) + (2p^2 - 2p + 3)$

15. $(3g^2 + 3g + 5) + (5g^2 - 3)$

16. $(5r^2 - 6) + (-r^2 - 4r + 7)$

13-2 Skills Practice

Adding Polynomials

Find each sum.

1. $5q + 7$
   $(+)\ 2q - 2$

2. $7f - 10$
   $(+) - 2f + 3$

3. $r^2 - 3r$
   $(+)\ r^2 + 4r - 1$

4. $9n^2 - 3n$
   $(+)\quad 3n - 5$

5. $w^2 - 3w + 3$
   $(+)\ w^2 + 4w + 1$

6. $8c^2 - 4c + 6$
   $(+)\ c^2 +\ c - 1$

7. $-p^2 + 6p + 8$
   $(+)\ p^2 - 4p - 5$

8. $3v^2 + v$
   $(+) -2v + 7$

9. $6m^2 +\ m + 1$
   $(+)2m^2 - 2m - 3$

10. $5d^2 + 7d - 4$
    $(+)\ 5d^2 - 6d - 4$

11. $(2r^2 - 3) + (-r^2 + 4r + 1)$

12. $(g^2 + 2g + 5) + (5g^2 - 2g + 3)$

13. $(-m - 9) + (3m - 3)$

14. $(2x^2 + 8x - 7) + (3x + 5)$

15. $(k^2 - k) + (7k^2 - k - 2)$

16. $(4a^2 + 3ab) + (ab + 2b^2)$

17. $(5c - 7) + (3c^2 - 4c + 6)$

18. $(x^2 + xy) + (xy + y^2)$

19. $(-h^2 + 3h - 6) + (4h^2 - 2h + 3)$

20. $(x^2 + x + 1) + (2x - 9x^2)$

21. $(6g^2 - 2g - 3) + (2g^2 + 5g)$

22. $(b^2 + b + 1) + (b^2 - b - 1)$

23. $(2y^2 - 7y + 9) + (y^2 - 4y - 6)$

24. $(7p^3 - 4) + (2p^2 + 5p + 1)$

13-2 **Practice**

Adding Polynomials

Find each sum.

1. $8q + 3$
    $(+) \, 4q - 2$

2. $9f - 3$
    $(+) \, -f - 15$

3. $4r^2 + 11r$
    $(+) \, 5r^2 - 3r - 7$

4. $n^2 - 3n$
    $(+) 3n - 10$

5. $6w^2 + 2w + 7$
    $(+) \, 8w^2 + 3w - 9$

6. $8c^2 - 3c + 15$
    $(+) \, 3c^2 + 3c - 11$

7. $-5p^2 - 2p + 4$
    $(+) \, 5p^2 + 2p - 4$

8. $7v^2 - 2v$
    $(+) \, 7v^2 - v + 5$

9. $5m^2 + 6m - 3$
    $(+) \, 8m^2 + 9m - 2$

10. $7d^2 + 8d - 3$
    $(+) \, d^2 + d + 3$

11. $(r^2 + 9) + (-4r^2 + 6r + 10)$

12. $(g^2 + 3g - 6) + (6g^2 - 6g + 1)$

13. $(-2m + 10) + (5m - 3)$

14. $(4x^2 - 7x) + (8x + 5)$

15. $(3k^2 + 9k) + (k^2 - 2k - 4)$

16. $(2a^2 - 3ab) + (4ab - 8b^2)$

17. $(c + 4) + (c^2 - c + 6)$

18. $(5x^2 - 3xy) + (2xy + 9y^2)$

19. $(2y^3 + y^2 + 5) + (2y^2 + 3y)$

20. $(-5p^2 + 6p - 7) + (p^2 - 2)$

21. $(3ab^2 - 2a - 1) + (a^2 + ab + 3)$

22. $(6rs^3 + 4r) + (5rs^3 + 7)$

23. **GEOMETRY** The lengths of the sides of a triangle are $(x^2 - 5)$, $(7x - 1)$, and x. Find the perimeter of the triangle.

13-2 Word Problem Practice

Adding Polynomials

1. **TELEPHONE PLAN** A phone plan with XYZ Cellular costs $49 per month, with additional fees of t per text message and e per minute for any extra minutes not covered by the plan. Aaron sent 13 text messages and used 7 extra minutes in January, and sent 8 text messages and used 27 extra minutes in February. Write an expression representing Aaron's two month telephone bill.

2. **GARDENING** Marty and Jack are planning a vegetable garden together. They decide that they want a design with six square pieces in the middle and a 3-foot border around the outside. Write an expression that represents the area of the garden.

3. **SNACK SALE** Susanna and Winston held a snack sale to raise money for a class trip. They sold drinks for d dollars each and snacks for s dollars each. Starting with $30 to begin with, they sold items according to the table. Write an expression that represents how much money they had at the end of the snack sale.

Item	Number Sold
Lemonade	20
Fruit Punch	34
Apple	18
Pretzel	9
Granola Bar	28

4. **ANCIENT ART** A *mosaic* is a panel made up of objects, such as broken glass or seashells, that form a design. One method for producing mosaic, which the ancient Greeks and Romans often used, was to press tiles into grout. Held in place by the grout, some of the designs have survived for thousands of years. Suppose an artisan wanted to create a square mosaic panel measuring x inches on a side by first lining the edges with a row of tiles that measured 1 inch square. Write an expression to represent the number of square edge tiles needed for the panel. Sample answers:

$x = 6$

PRINT SHOP For Exercises 5 and 6, use the following information.

A small business provides a photocopying and printing service for its customers. Its prices are listed in the table.

Product	Price Each
Greeting Card	$0.50
Folded Brochure	$1.00
Poster	$4.25

5. Write the polynomial expression that represents the total cost of a print job that includes c cards, b brochures, and p posters.

6. If a copy job costs $232.50 in total and includes 100 greeting cards and 55 brochures, how many posters were included?

Lesson 13-2

13-2 Enrichment

Adding Polynomials

Can you make a sentence using these words?

A FRUIT TIME LIKE AN BUT FLIES BANANA ARROW LIKE FLIES

Add the polynomials. Then find the word in the table at the right that corresponds to the sum. Read the words in order down the column to discover the hidden saying.

Word

1. $(2x^2 + 3x^2) + (5x^2 + x^2)$

2. $(2x^2 + 3x^3) + (5x^2 + x^2)$

3. $(2x^2 + x) + (xy + x)$

4. $(x^3 + 2x^2) + (5x^3 + x)$

5. $(x + xy) + (x^2 + xy)$

6. $(5x^2 + x) + (x + 2x^4)$

7. $(xy + y^2 + x^2) + (2xy + x^2)$

8. $(3x^2 + 2x^3) + (x^3 + x)$

9. $(x + x^2) + x^3$

10. $(x^3 + x^3) + (x^3 + x^3)$

11. $2x^{12} + 2x^{12}$

$4x^3$	A
$2x^2 + 3xy + y^2$	FRUIT
$11x^2$	TIME
$x^3 + x^2 + x$	LIKE
$6x^3 + 2x^2 + x$	AN
$2x^4 + 5x^2 + 2x$	BUT
$3x^3 + 8x^2$	FLIES
$4x^{12}$	BANANA
$x^2 + 2xy + x$	ARROW
$2x^2 + 2x + xy$	LIKE
$3x^3 + 3x^2 + x$	FLIES

13-3 Lesson Reading Guide

Subtracting Polynomials

Get Ready for the Lesson

Read the introduction to Lesson 13-3 in your textbook. Write your answers below.

a. What is the difference in degrees and the difference in minutes between the two stations?

b. Explain how you can find the difference in latitude between any two locations, given the degrees and minutes.

c. The longitude of Station 1 is $162°16'36''$ and the longitude of Station 5 is $68°8'2''$. Find the difference in longitude between the two stations.

Read the Lesson

1. Show how to find the difference $(3x^2 + x + 2) - (2x^2 - 7)$ by aligning like terms and by adding the additive inverse.

Like Terms   **Additive Inverse**

2. Which method do you prefer? Why?

Remember What You Learned

3. a. You have learned to subtract polynomials by adding the additive inverse. Look up *inverse* in the dictionary. What is its definition? How does this help you remember how to find the additive inverse?

b. Write the additive inverses of the polynomials in the table below.

Polynomial	Additive Inverse
$x^2 + 2x - 3$	
$6x - 8$	
$5x^2 + 8y^2 - 2xy$	

Lesson 13-3

13-3 Study Guide and Intervention

Subtracting Polynomials

Subtract Polynomials To subtract polynomials, subtract like terms.

Example Find $(x^2 + 3x - 6) - (4x^2 - 1)$.

Method 1 Subtract vertically.

$$\begin{array}{r} x^2 + 3x - 6 \\ (-)\ 4x^2 \qquad - 1 \\ \hline -3x^2 + 3x - 5 \end{array}$$

Method 2 Add the additive inverse of $4x^2 - 1$, which is $(-1)(4x^2 - 1)$ or $-4x^2 + 1$.

$$= (x^2 + 3x - 6) - (4x^2 - 1)$$
$$= (x^2 + 3x - 6) + (-4x^2 + 1)$$
$$= (x^2 - 4x^2) + (3x) + (-6 + 1)$$
$$= -3x^2 + 3x - 5$$

Exercises

Find each difference.

1.
$$\begin{array}{r} 4c + 7 \\ (-)\ 3c + 3 \\ \hline \end{array}$$

2.
$$\begin{array}{r} 2m + 5 \\ (-)\ -8m + 1 \\ \hline \end{array}$$

3.
$$\begin{array}{r} 9k^2 - 4k + 5 \\ (-)\ \ k^2 \qquad - 5 \\ \hline \end{array}$$

4.
$$\begin{array}{r} 3z^2 - z \\ (-)\ \qquad 3z - 5 \\ \hline \end{array}$$

5. $(-6r + 3) - (7r + 2)$

6. $(8f^2 - 7f - 3) - (2f + 4)$

7. $(5n^2 - 2n) - (3n + 9)$

8. $(a^2 + 5ab) - (-2ab - 3b^2)$

9. $(6g^2 + 8) - (5g^2 - 2g + 6)$

10. $(8x^2 - 3y) - (2xy + 3y)$

11. $(n - 12) - (n^2 + n + 9)$

12. $(h^2 - 2h + 1) - (3h - 7h^2)$

13. $(y^2 + y + 1) - (y^2 - y + 1)$

14. $(6p^2 - 5p - 1) - (2p - 4)$

15. $(4q^2 + q) - (q^2 + 3)$

16. $(6v^2 + 8) - (7v^2 + 2v - 5)$

17. $(u^2 + u - 4) - (5u^2 - 4)$

18. $(9b^2 + 2) - (-b^2 + b + 9)$

13-3 Skills Practice

Subtracting Polynomials

Find each difference.

1. $7y + 5$
   $(-)\ y + 6$

2. $k + 8$
   $(-)\ 2k - 9$

3. $w^2 + \ w + 1$
   $(-)\ 2w^2 + 3w + 2$

4. $c^2 - 7c + 2$
   $(-)\ -c^2 - \ c - 1$

5. $3d^2 - \ d$
   $(-)\ d^2 - 3d - 8$

6. $7n^2 - 3n$
   $(-)\ -n^2 - 3n - 1$

7. $2m^2 - 5m + 3$
   $(-)\ 5m^2 - \ m - 3$

8. $d^2 - 3d - 6$
   $(-)\ d^2 - 2d - 1$

9. $-q^2 + 2q + 2$
   $(-)\ q^2 - 7q + 9$

10. $v^2 + \ v$
    $(-)\ 8v^2 - 8v + 8$

11. $(r^2 - 10r - 3) - (-r^2 - r + 1)$

12. $(7k^2 + k + 8) - (2k^2 - 3k - 3)$

13. $(a^2 - 9) - (a - 4)$

14. $(4x^2 + 11x - 7) - (x^2 - 3x - 6)$

15. $(k^2 - 3k) - (2k^2 - 7k - 1)$

16. $(5a^2 + ab) - (ab + 3b^2)$

17. $(5u^2 - 7) - (3u^2 - 4u + 6)$

18. $(4m^2 + mn) - (3mn + n^2)$

19. $(h^2 + 3h - 6) - (h^2 - 2h - 3)$

20. $(x^2 - x - 1) - (2x + 9x^2)$

21. $(6g^2 + 3g + 3) - (g^2 + g - 5)$

22. $(b^2 + b + 1) - (b^2 - b - 1)$

23. $(a^2 - 9a - 10) - (a^2 - a - 4)$

24. $(4r^2 + 7r) - (3r^2 - 2r + 7)$

Lesson 13-3

13-3 Practice

Subtracting Polynomials

Find each difference.

1. $\begin{array}{r} 4y + 1 \\ (-)\ 3y + 8 \\ \hline \end{array}$

2. $\begin{array}{r} 2k + 3 \\ (-)\ 7k - 6 \\ \hline \end{array}$

3. $\begin{array}{r} 5j^2 + 2j - 2 \\ (-)\ j^2 + 9j + 2 \\ \hline \end{array}$

4. $\begin{array}{r} c^2 + 5c - 3 \\ (-)\ -c^2 - 5c - 1 \\ \hline \end{array}$

5. $\begin{array}{r} d^2 - 4d + 6 \\ (-)\ d^2 + 3d - 8 \\ \hline \end{array}$

6. $\begin{array}{r} 2n^2 - 3n - 10 \\ (-)\ -n^2 - 3n + 8 \\ \hline \end{array}$

7. $\begin{array}{r} 9m^2 - 4m + 13 \\ (-)\ 7m^2 - 2m - 3 \\ \hline \end{array}$

8. $\begin{array}{r} d^2 + 3d - 6 \\ (-)\ d^2 + 3d + 6 \\ \hline \end{array}$

9. $\begin{array}{r} -6q^2 - 3q + 2 \\ (-)\ 3q^2 + 4q + 4 \\ \hline \end{array}$

10. $\begin{array}{r} v^2 - v \\ (-)\ 2v^2 - 9v - 3 \\ \hline \end{array}$

11. $(4n^2 - n - 6) - (-2n^2 - 3n - 14)$

12. $(3k^2 + 9k) - (8k^2 - 12)$

13. $(k^2 - 7) - (k - 11)$

14. $(9x^2 - x - 2) - (3x^2 - x - 4)$

15. $(k^2 - 12) - (k^2 + 6k - 9)$

16. $(k^2 + 4kb) - (5kb + 2b^2)$

17. $(3u^2 - 9) - (u^2 + 21u + 2)$

18. $(5m^2 - 4mn) - (4mn + 8n^2)$

19. $(h^2 + 8h + 5) - (h^2 - 3h - 7)$

20. $(2x^2 - 4x - 8) - (2x - 8x^2)$

21. $(6g^2 + 3g + 2) - (g^2 + g - 4)$

22. $(b^3 + b^2 - ab) - (b^3 + 3b^2 + 5)$

23. **POOLS** A swimming pool is $(4w^2 - 16)$ feet long and $(w - 16)$ feet wide. How much longer is the length than the width?

13-3 Word Problem Practice

Subtracting Polynomials

1. GEOGRAPHY The highest point in the state of Oklahoma is Black Mesa and the lowest point is the Little River. The difference in elevation between these two points is 176 meters more than the sum of the elevations. What is the elevation of the lowest point in Oklahoma?

2. TAXI FARES The rate for a taxicab in Austin is $3.50 for the first mile plus $2 for each additional mile. In Houston, the taxi rate is $4 for the first mile and $1.80 for every mile thereafter. What is the difference between the taxi rates of these two cities?

3. GEOMETRY The perimeter of the isosceles triangle is $8x - 3$ inches. Find the length of the third side.

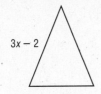
$3x - 2$

4. POSTERS Pam and her friends are making a poster for the clothing drive at school. They decide on the design below. Each rectangle will be outlined with ribbon. Write an expression to show how much more ribbon Pam and her friends will need for the larger rectangle than for the smaller one.

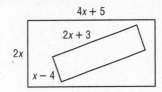
$4x + 5$
$2x + 3$
$2x$
$x - 4$

INTERIOR DECORATING For Exercises 5 and 6, use the following information.

Shayla is putting up a wallpaper border on the walls in her room. The border comes in pieces that are x feet long. Shayla figures that she will need 4 pieces plus an extra 3 feet of border to trim the long wall of her room.

5. Write the polynomial expression that represents the length of her room.

6. The total amount of border Shayla used was $14x + 10$ feet. Write the polynomial expression that represents the width of her room.

Lesson 13-3

13-3 Enrichment

Polynomials with Fractional Coefficients

Polynomials may have fractional coefficients in some or all of the terms. Computation with these types of polynomials is done in the same way as with whole-number coefficients.

Add or subtract. Write all coefficients as fractions.

1. Add $\frac{3}{4}x^2 + \frac{2}{5}y^2$ and $\frac{1}{6}x^2 - \frac{4}{3}y^2$.

2. From $\frac{1}{2}x^2 - \frac{1}{3}xy^2 + \frac{1}{4}y^2$, take $\frac{1}{3}x^2 - \frac{1}{2}xy + \frac{5}{6}y^2$.

3. Add $\frac{3}{2}x - \frac{4}{3}y$, $-\frac{7}{8}x - \frac{6}{7}y$, and $y - \frac{1}{4}x$.

4. Subtract $\frac{1}{6}x^2 + \frac{1}{8}x - \frac{1}{4}$ from $\frac{2}{3}x^2 + \frac{5}{8}x + \frac{1}{2}$.

5. Add $\frac{1}{3}xy + \frac{11}{12}y^2$ to $\frac{4}{9}xy - \frac{1}{6}y^2$.

6. Add $\frac{1}{5}x^2 - \frac{1}{8}x - \frac{1}{3}$ and $\frac{3}{10}x^2 + \frac{5}{8}x + \frac{1}{9}$.

7. From $\frac{1}{2} + \frac{2}{3}y + \frac{3}{4}y^2$, take $\frac{1}{8} + \frac{1}{6}y - \frac{5}{6}y^2$.

8. Subtract $\frac{7}{12}x - \frac{1}{4}$ from $\frac{3}{4}x - \frac{1}{3}$.

9. Add $\frac{3}{8}x^2 - \frac{1}{3}xy + \frac{5}{9}y^2$ and $\frac{1}{2}x^2 - \frac{1}{2}xy - \frac{1}{3}y^2$.

10. Subtract $\frac{3}{4}y^2 + \frac{1}{2}y$ from $\frac{4}{3}y^2 + \frac{7}{8}y$.

13-4 Lesson Reading Guide

Multiplying a Polynomial by a Monomial

Get Ready for the Lesson

Read the introduction to Lesson 13-4 in your textbook. Write your answers below.

a. Write an expression that represents the area of the rectangular region outlined on the photo.

b. Recall that $2(4 + 1) = 2(4) + 2(1)$ by the Distributive Property. Use this property to simplify the expression you wrote in part **a**.

c. The Grande Arche is approximately w feet deep. Explain how you can write a polynomial to represent the volume of the hollowed-out region of the building. Then write the polynomial.

Read the Lesson

1. Draw a model that shows the product $x(x + 2)$. Write the polynomial that shows the product.

2. Explain the Distributive Property and give an example of how it is used to multiply a polynomial by a monomial.

Remember What You Learned

3. *Distribute* is a common word in the English language.

    a. Find the definition of *distribute* in a dictionary. Write the definition that most closely relates to this lesson.

    b. Explain how this definition can help you remember how to use the Distributive Property to multiply a polynomial by a monomial.

Lesson 13-4

13-4 Study Guide and Intervention

Multiplying a Polynomial by a Monomial

The Distributive Property can be used to multiply a polynomial by a monomial.

Example 1 Find $7(4x - 8)$.

$7(4x - 8) = 7(4x) - 7(8)$
$= 28x - 56$

Example 2 Find $(x^2 - 5x + 4)(-2x)$.

$(x^2 - 5x + 4)(-2x) = x^2(-2x) - 5x(-2x) + 4(-2x)$
$= -2x^3 + 10x^2 - 8x$

Exercises

Find each product.

1. $5(7y + 4)$

2. $(3h + 6)4$

3. $-9(q + 8)$

4. $6(d - 2)$

5. $(4g - 5)(-2)$

6. $-7(4x^2 - 7)$

7. $-2(n^2 - 3n + 9)$

8. $(a^2 - 2ab + b^2)5$

9. $r(r + 9)$

10. $(b^2 - 4)(-b)$

11. $-x(3x + 6)$

12. $(2k - 9)(k^2)$

13. $-m(6m + 1)$

14. $p(7p - 2)$

15. $(8 - 3h)(-h)$

16. $w(4w^2 - 2w + 3)$

17. $ab(2a + b)$

18. $x(7x + y)$

19. $(m^2 - mn - n)m$

20. $2y(5y + 1)$

21. $-10u(u - 5)$

22. $(5r^2 - 2r)(-3r)$

23. $8z(2z + 7)$

24. $5b^2(6b - 2)$

25. $4p^2(6p^2 + 3p)$

26. $(5v^2 - 2v - 4)(-2v)$

27. $8y^3(3y^2 - y + 8)$

28. $3m(2m + 4n)$

29. $(8gh - 3h)(-3gh)$

30. $5a(2a - 3ab + b)$

13-4 Skills Practice

Multiplying a Polynomial by a Monomial

Find each product.

1. $4(k + 7)$

2. $(5h + 3)3$

3. $-9(2q + 7)$

4. $(6v - 1)(-6)$

5. $-8(5h - 6)$

6. $3(12y - 6)$

7. $(9d + 3)4$

8. $-5(5n - 9)$

9. $2(x^2 + 4)$

10. $-6(5x^2 - 3x)$

11. $(4x^2 - 6x - 9)9$

12. $-7(2c^2 - 8c + 5)$

13. $g(2g + 5)$

14. $-b(9b - 6)$

15. $(4y + 7)y$

16. $(2j - 1)(-j)$

17. $-c(c - 2)$

18. $h(6h + 4)$

19. $(6k + 6)(-k)$

20. $p(3p - 8)$

21. $-a(8a + 2)$

22. $r(r^2 + 7r)$

23. $x(4x^2 - 2x - 1)$

24. $ab(3ab + 2a)$

25. $x(4xy - 3y^2)$

26. $(gh - h)(-g)$

27. $x(4x^2 - xy + y^2)$

28. $6v(3v + 9)$

29. $(u + 4)(-5u)$

30. $8b(b - 6)$

31. $-7d(5d - 9)$

32. $(8w - 4)w$

33. $a(7a + 4)$

34. $(6y - 6)(-y^2)$

35. $s(s + 1)$

36. $-m(6m - 7)$

37. $-k^2(2k - 3)$

38. $c(7c^2 + 3c - 4)$

39. $7mn(m + 2mn + 4n)$

40. $8a(a + ab + b)$

41. $(xy - y^2)(-4xy)$

42. $-8u(7u^2 - 2uv + 4v^2)$

Lesson 13-4

13-4 **Practice**

Multiplying a Polynomial by a Monomial

Find each product.

1. $5(3k + 8)$

2. $(3h + 6)2$

3. $-2(q - 4)$

4. $(3v - 5)(-7)$

5. $11(4d - 7)$

6. $-8(12c - 6)$

7. $(5g - 10)(-5)$

8. $2(5p - 10)$

9. $-9(3f^2 - 2f - 1)$

10. $2.5(8w + 5)$

11. $(4r^3 - 3r)(-8)$

12. $-6(3x^2 - 2x + 7)$

13. $n(7n + 3)$

14. $(6u - 15)(-u)$

15. $-h(8h + 2)$

16. $(8y + 3)(-y)$

17. $a(4a - 4)$

18. $(5p + 15)(-p)$

19. $-d(-5d + 1)$

20. $-g(1.8g + 10)$

21. $m(0.9m^2 - 0.5)$

22. $(2q^3 - 5q^2 - 2q)(-q)$

23. $k^3(7k^4 - 2k^2 + 6)$

24. $ab(10a^2b + 3a)$

25. $y^2(5x - 2xy + y)$

26. $n(8 - m - 12mn^2)$

27. $(4gh^2 - 2g^2 - h)(-g^2)$

28. $(20q - 4)(-2q)$

29. $14k(2k + 5)$

30. $(9p - 7)(-3p^2)$

31. $(0.2c - 1)(-1.5c^2)$

32. $-6.5n(4n^2 - 8)$

33. $-6x^2(4x^2 - 10x)$

34. $5h^2(2h^3 - h^2 - 7h + 8)$

35. $(4y^2 - 3y + 9)(-2y)$

36. $6gh(8g^2 + 4gh + 3h^2)$

37. $10a(2a^2 - 5ab + 4a)$

38. $(8x^2 - 3xy - xy^2)(-7x)$

39. $-5c^2(2cd - d^2 + 1)$

40. Find the area of a porch that is $3x$ feet wide and $4x + 9$ feet long.

13-4 Word Problem Practice

Multiplying a Polynomial by a Monomial

1. **BOOKS** The largest published book in the world is Michael Hawley's *Bhutan: A Visual Odyssey Across the Kingdom*. The length of a page is 3 feet shorter than twice its width. The perimeter of a page is 24 feet. What are the dimensions of the book?

2. **GEOMETRY** Find the area of the shaded region. Write in simplest form.

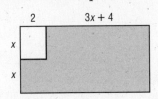

3. **FOOTBALL** The dimensions of Canadian football fields are different than the dimensions of American football fields. Use the information in the table to find the length and width of each football field.

Playing Field Plus End Zones		
Measure	**American (ft)**	**Canadian (ft)**
Perimeter	1040	1290
Width	w	w
Length	$2w + 40$	$(2w + 40) + 20$

4. **FLAGS** The largest flag flown from a flagstaff is a Brazilian national flag in Brasilia, Brazil. The width of the flag is 20 meters more than half the length. Find the area of the flag. Write in simplest form

MANUFACTURING For Exercises 5–7, use the following information.

Casey's Cardboard Company makes different sizes of cardboard boxes. The figure below shows a template for one size cardboard box before it has been cut and folded.

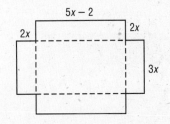

5. Write a simplified expression to represent the surface area of the cardboard box.

6. Find the surface area of the box if x is 4 inches.

7. Suppose a side is extended to so the box will be completely enclosed when it is put together. Write a simplified expression to represent the surface area of the enclosed box.

Lesson 13-4

13-4 Enrichment

Polynomials and Volume

The volume of a rectangular prism can be written as the product of three polynomials. Recall that the volume equals the length times the width times the height.

The two prisms at the right represent the cube of y and the cube of x.

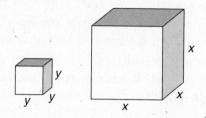

Multiply to find the volume of each prism. Write each answer as an algebraic expression.

1.
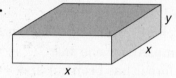

2.
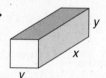

3.
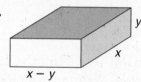

4.
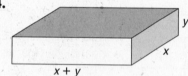

5.
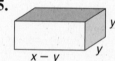

6.
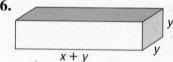

Multiply, then add to find each volume. Write each answer as an algebraic expression.

7.
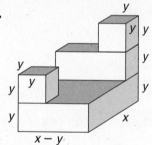

8.
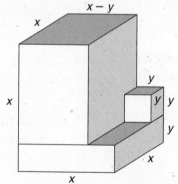

9.
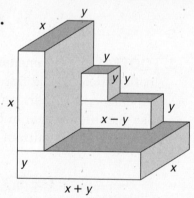

13-4 Graphing Calculator Activity

Polynomials

A graphing calculator can be used to verify solutions to polynomial arithmetic.

Example 1 **Find each sum or difference.**

a. $(8x - 6) + (-9x + 11)$

First, find the sum.
$(8x - 6) + (-9x + 11) = -x + 5$
To verify the solution, enter the original expression, $(8x - 6) + (-9x + 11)$, into **Y1** and the sum, $-x + 5$, into **Y2**. Compare the graphs of both.

Keystrokes:

11 [ )] [ENTER] [(-)] [X,T,θ,n] [+] 5 [ZOOM] 6.

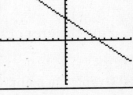
[−10, 10] scl:1 by [−10, 10] scl:1

The graphs coincide, so the expressions are equivalent. Thus, the solution is correct.

b. $4a^2 + 7a + 4 - (3a^2 + 2)$

Find the difference.
$4a^2 + 7a + 4 - (3a^2 + 2) = a^2 + 7a + 2$
Enter the original expression into **Y1** and the difference in **Y2**. Compare the graphs.

Keystrokes: [Y=] [X,T,θ,n] [x²] [+] 7 [X,T,θ,n] [+] 4 [−] [( ] 3 [X,T,θ,n]
[x²] [+] 2 [ )] [ENTER] [X,T,θ,n] [x²] [+] 7 [X,T,θ,n] [+] 2 [GRAPH] .

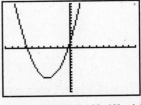
[−10, 10] scl:1 by [−10, 10] scl:1

The graphs coincide, so the expressions are equivalent. Thus, the solution is correct.

Example 2 **Find $5a(2a + 3)$.**

Find the product.
$5a(2a + 3) = 10a^2 + 15a$
Enter the original expression into **Y1** and the solution into **Y2**. Compare the graphs.

Keystrokes: [Y=] 5 [X,T,θ,n] [x²] [( ] 2 [X,T,θ,n] [+] 3 [ )] [ENTER] 10 [X,T,θ,n]
[X,T,θ,n] [+] 15 [X,T,θ,n] [GRAPH] .

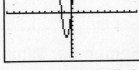
[−10, 10] scl:1 by [−10, 10] scl:1

The graphs coincide, so the expressions are equivalent. Thus, the solution is correct.

Exercises

Perform the stated operation.

1. $(x^2 + 4x + 12) + (-5x^2 + 8)$

2. $(16x^2 + 3x + 9) - (2x^2 + 8x + 1)$

3. $7(-2x^2 + 5x - 11)$

4. $6x(-2x^2 + 8x + 2)$

Lesson 13-4

13-5   Lesson Reading Guide

Linear and Nonlinear Functions

Get Ready for the Lesson

Read the introduction to Lesson 13-5 in your textbook. Write your answers below.

a. Write an expression to represent the area of the deck.

b. Find the area of the deck for widths of 6, 8, 10, 12, and 14 feet.

c. Graph the points whose ordered pairs are (width, area). Do the points fall along a straight line? Explain.

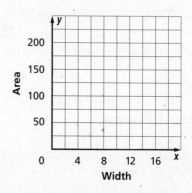

Read the Lesson

Write a definition and give an example of each new vocabulary phrase.

Vocabulary	Definition	Example
1. nonlinear function		
2. quadratic function		
3. cubic function		

Remember What You Learned

4. You have learned about linear and nonlinear functions. Nonlinear functions include quadratic functions and cubic functions. Below, write three equations that represent each type of function given. For the nonlinear functions, include at least one quadratic function and one cubic function.

Linear

1.

2.

3.

Nonlinear

1.

2.

3.

13-5 Study Guide and Intervention

Linear and Nonlinear Functions

Linear functions have constant rates of change. Their graphs are straight lines and their equations can be written in the form $y = mx + b$. Nonlinear functions do not have constant rates of change and their graphs are not straight lines.

Example 1 Determine whether each equation represents a *linear* or *nonlinear* function.

a. $y = 9$

This is linear because it can be written as $y = 0x + 9$.

b. $y = x^2 + 4$

This is nonlinear because the exponent of x is not 1, so the equation cannot be written in the form $y = mx + b$.

Tables can represent functions. A nonlinear function does not increase or decrease at a constant rate.

Example 2 Determine whether each table represents a *linear* or *nonlinear* function.

a.

x	y
0	−7
2	1
4	9
6	17

+2 (0→2), +2 (2→4), +2 (4→6) ; +8, +8, +8

As x increases by 2, y increases by 8. The rate of change is constant, so this is a linear function.

b.

x	y
0	100
5	75
10	0
15	−125

+5, +5, +5 ; −25, −75, −125

As x increases by 5, y decreases by a greater amount each time. The rate of change is not constant, so this is a nonlinear function.

Exercises

Determine whether each equation or table represents a *linear* or *nonlinear* function. Explain.

1. $x + 3y = 9$

2. $y = \dfrac{8}{x}$

3. $y = 6x(x + 1)$

4. $y = 9 - 5x$

5.

x	y
0	24
2	14
4	4
6	−6

6.

x	y
1	1
2	8
3	27
4	64

Lesson 13-5

13-5 Skills Practice

Linear and Nonlinear Functions

Determine whether each graph, equation, or table represents a *linear* or *nonlinear* function. Explain.

1.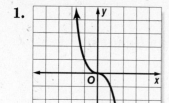

2.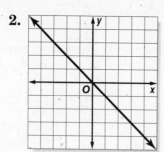

3.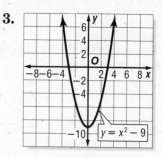

4. $y = \dfrac{x}{2} + 1$

5. $y = \dfrac{2}{x} + 10$

6. $y = 8x$

7. $y = 6$

8. $2x - y = 5$

9. $y = x^2 + 4$

10. $y + 4x^2 - 1 = 0$

11. $2y - 8x + 11 = 0$

12. $y = \sqrt{3x} - 2$

13.

x	y
1	8
2	5
3	2
4	−1

14.

x	y
6	1
12	3
18	6
24	10

15.

x	y
20	−4
15	−2
10	0
5	2

13-5 Practice

Linear and Nonlinear Functions

Determine whether each graph, equation, or table represents a *linear* or *nonlinear* function. Explain.

1.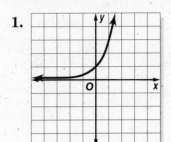

2.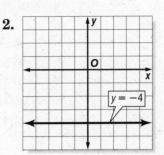

3.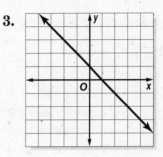

4. $5x - y = 15$

5. $3y + 12x^2 = 0$

6. $5y - x + 3 = 0$

7. $y = 6\sqrt{x} + 10$

8. $y = \dfrac{8}{x}$

9. $y = -x^2 + 2$

10.

x	y
1	1.0
2	0.8
3	0.6
4	0.4

11.

x	y
44	0
48	2.5
52	5.0
56	7.5

12.

x	y
3	1
6	-2
9	-5
12	-14

13. **GEOMETRY** The graph shows how the area of a square increases as the perimeter increases. Is this relationship linear or nonlinear? Explain.

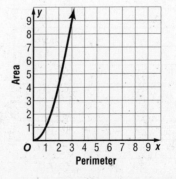

Lesson 13-5

13-5 Word Problem Practice

Linear and Nonlinear Functions

1. **TEMPERATURE** In the United States, temperature is most often measured in degrees Fahrenheit. Temperature is measured in degrees Celsius in the metric system. The formula used to convert between these two units of measure is $F = \dfrac{9}{5}C + 32$ where F represents degrees Fahrenheit and C represents degrees Celsius. Does this equation represent a *linear* or *nonlinear* function?

2. **COMPUTER GAMES** Suppose the function $-0.005d^2 + 0.12d = h$ is used to simulate the path of a golf ball that is hit off a tee in a computer game. Does this equation represent a *linear* or *nonlinear* function?

3. **GASOLINE** The table below shows gasoline prices in Springfield during a one-month period. Is the change in gas price a linear function? Explain.

Day of the Month	Price per Gallon
1	$2.57
4	$2.72
7	$2.72
10	$2.88
13	$2.88
16	$2.84
19	$2.76
21	$2.72
24	$2.64
27	$2.60
30	$2.52

4. **FOOTBALL PUNTS** The function $h = -16t^2 + 90t + 1.5$ represents the height h of the football, in feet, after t seconds when a punter kicks the ball with an upward velocity of 90 feet per second and his foot meets the ball 1.5 feet off the ground. Is this a linear function of time? Explain.

FLIGHT RESEARCH For Exercises 5 and 6, use the following information.

The equation $h = -16t^2 + 608t + 4482$ represents the height, h, in feet, of a pilot over time, t, in seconds, after he or she has ejected from a jet and falls to Earth with the aid of a parachute. A pilot is flying at an altitude of approximately 10,000 feet and is forced to eject from the jet. The equation $h = 10,000$ represents an altitude of 10,000 feet.

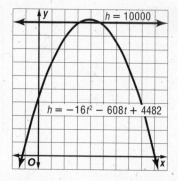

5. Which equation is a linear function?

6. Explain why the other equation is a nonlinear function.

13-5 Enrichment

David R. Hedgley

African-American mathematician David R. Hedgley, Jr. (1937–   )
solved one of the most difficult problems in the field of computer
graphics—how to program a computer to show any
three-dimensional object from a given viewpoint
just as the eye would see it. Hedgley's solution
helped researchers in aircraft experimentation.
Hedgley received an M.S. in Mathematics
from California State University in 1970 and
a Ph.D. in Computer Science from Somerset
University in England in 1988. Hedgley has
received numerous national achievement awards.

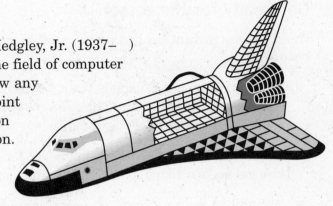

Polynomials in three variables are needed to describe some three-dimensional objects.
Each variable represents one of the three dimensions: height, width, and depth.

$P_1: x^2 + y^2 + z^2 + 10x + 4y + 2z - 19$

$P_2: 2x^2 + 2y^2 + 2z^2 - 2x - 3y + 5z - 2$

1. Add the polynomials P_1 and P_2.

2. Subtract the polynomials, P_1 from P_2.

If the polynomials above were each set equal to zero, they would form equations describing
two different spheres in three-dimensional space, or *3-space*. The coordinate plane you
studied in Chapter 2 represents *two-space*. You described most lines in that plane by
an equation in two variables. Each point on a line could be written as an ordered pair
of numbers (x, y). Each point on any figure in 3-space can be written as an *ordered triple*
of numbers (x, y, z).

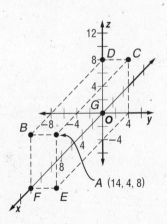

3. What are the values of x, y, and z for point A in the diagram?

4. Give the ordered triple representing each of the points
  B through G in the diagram.

Lesson 13-5

13-6 **Lesson Reading Guide**

Graphing Quadratic and Cubic Functions

Get Ready for the Lesson

Read the introduction to Lesson 13-6 in your textbook. Write your answers below.

a. The volume of cube V equals the cube of the length of an edge a. Write a formula to represent the volume of a cube as a function of edge length.

b. Graph the volume as a function of edge length. (*Hint*: Use values of a like 0, 0.5, 1, 1.5, 2, and so on.)

c. Would it be reasonable to use negative numbers for x values in this situation?

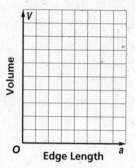

Read the Lesson

1. Write a quadratic function. Explain what makes it a quadratic function and what its graph would look like.

2. Write a cubic function. Explain what makes it a cubic function and what its graph would look like.

Remember What You Learned

3. You have learned to graph quadratic and cubic functions. Make a list of the steps you use to graph the two functions.

13-6 Study Guide and Intervention

Graphing Quadratic and Cubic Functions

To graph a quadratic or cubic function, make a table of values and then plot the points.

Example   Graph $y = 2x^3 - 1$.

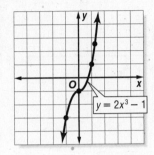

x	y
−1	−3
0	−1
1	1
1.2	2.5

Exercises

Graph each function.

1. $y = x^2 + 2$

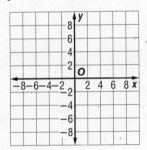

2. $y = x^3 + 2$

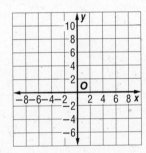

3. $y = -x^2 + 2$

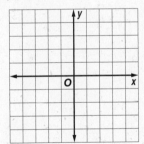

4. $y = -x^3 + 2$

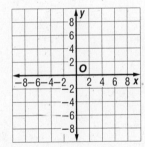

5. $y = x^2 - 2$

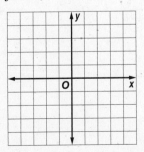

6. $y = x^3 - 2$

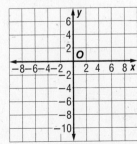

37

13-6 Skills Practice

Graphing Quadratic and Cubic Functions

Graph each function.

1. $y = 5x^2$

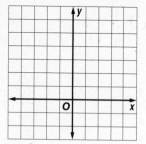

2. $y = 5x^3$

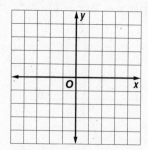

3. $y = -5x^2$

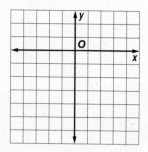

4. $y = -5x^3$

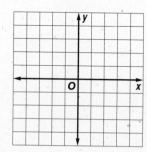

5. $y = x^2 + 4$

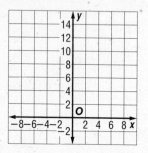

6. $y = x^3 + 4$

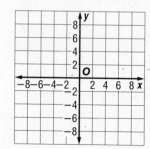

7. $y = x^2 - 4$

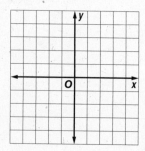

8. $y = x^3 - 4$

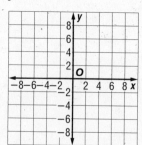

13-6 Practice

Graphing Quadratic and Cubic Functions

Graph each function.

1. $y = 0.4x^2$

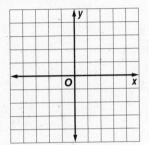

2. $y = 0.4x^3$

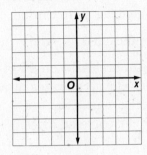

3. $y = -2x^2 - 1$

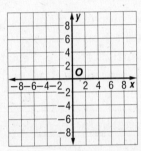

4. $y = -2x^3 - 1$

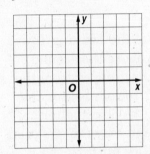

5. WINDOWS A window maker has 25 feet of wire to frame a window. One side of the window is x feet and the other side is $9 - x$ feet.

    a. Write an equation to represent the area A of the window.

    b. Graph the equation you wrote in part **a.**

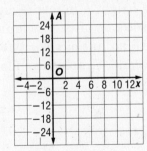

    c. If the area of the window is 18 square feet, what are the two possible values of x?

13-6 Word Problem Practice

Graphing Quadratic and Cubic Functions

1. RACING Between the ages of 8 and 16, Houston native Erica Enders won 37 junior dragster races. The distance her car travels down the drag strip can be expressed by the equation $d = \frac{1}{2}at^2$, where a is the rate of acceleration and t is time. Suppose her car accelerates at a rate of 49.5 feet per second. Find the number of feet her car traveled after 7 seconds.

2. PHYSICS The top of the Leaning Tower of Pisa is 185 feet above the ground. Suppose an object is dropped from the top of the Leaning Tower of Pisa. The height h in feet of the object, after t seconds, is represented by the equation $h = 185 - 16t^2$. How far from the ground is it after 3 seconds?

3. VISTAS The Texas State Capitol building is 311 feet tall. The formula $a = \frac{2}{3}d^2$ represents the number of miles d that a person can see from an altitude of a feet. Graph the function and use it to estimate how far you could see from the top of the Texas State Capitol.

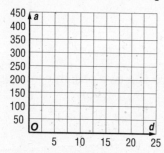

4. GEOMETRY Write the function for the volume of a cone as a function of a radius r units if the height equals the radius. Then graph the function.

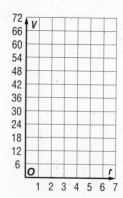

FIREWORKS For Exercises 5 and 6, use the following information.

The largest annual pyrotechnic display in North America is *Thunder over Louisville* held to kick off the Kentucky Derby Festival. The table shows the larger shell sizes and their corresponding velocities.

Shell Size (in.)	Initial Velocity (ft/sec)
8	235
10	263
12	287.5
24	393
36	481

Source: www.pyropage.net/physics.html

5. The equation $h = -16t^2 + 235t + 3$ represents the height h in feet of an 8-inch shell t seconds after it is launched from 3 feet with an initial velocity of 235 feet per second. Graph the equation.

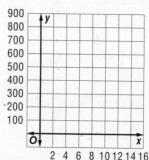

6. How high is the shell after 5 seconds?

13-6 Enrichment

Translating Quadratic Graphs

When a figure is moved to a new position without undergoing any rotation, then the figure is said to have been **translated** to the new position.

The graph of a quadratic equation in the form $y = (x - b)^2 + c$ is a translation of the graph of $y = x^2$.

Start with a graph of $y = x^2$.

Slide to the right 4 units.

$$y = (x - 4)^2$$

Then slide up 3 units.

$$y = (x - 4)^2 + 3$$

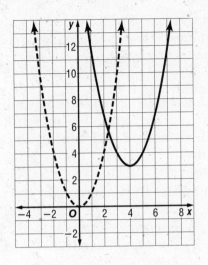

The following equations are in the form $y = x^2 + c$. Graph each equation.

1. $y = x^2 + 1$

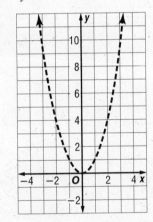

2. $y = x^2 + 2$

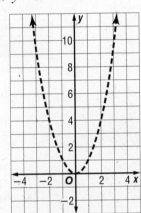

3. $y = x^2 - 2$

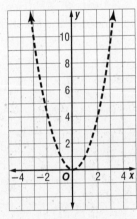

The following equations are in the form $y = (x - b)^2$. Graph each equation.

4. $y = (x - 1)^2$

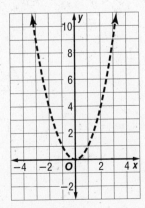

5. $y = (x - 3)^2$

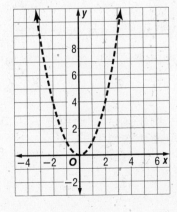

6. $y = (x + 2)^2$

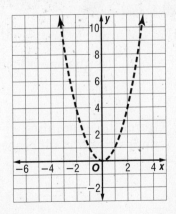

13-6 Spreadsheet Activity

Families of Quadratic Graphs

A *family of graphs* is a group of graphs that have at least one characteristic in common. You can use a spreadsheet to study the characteristics of families of quadratic graphs.

Example Graph the quadratics $y = x^2$, $y = 2x^2$, and $y = 4x^2$. What are the similarities and differences among the graphs?

Step 1 Use the Column A for the values of x and Columns B, C, and D for the values of y. Exponents are entered using the ^ symbol. For example, cell B2 contains the formula A2^2.

Step 2 To create a graph from the data, select the data in Columns A, B, C, and D and choose Chart from the Insert menu. Select an XY (Scatter) chart with a smooth line to show the graphs.

Quadratic.xls

	A	B	C	D
1	x	y=x^2	y=2x^2	y=4x^2
2	-5	25	50	100
3	-4	16	32	64
4	-3	9	18	36
5	-2	4	8	16
6	-1	1	2	4
7	0	0	0	0
8	1	1	2	4
9	2	4	8	16
10	3	9	18	36
11	4	16	32	64
12	5	25	50	100

Sheet 1 / Sheet 2 / Sheet 3

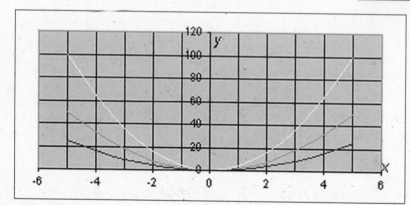

The graphs of all three functions pass through the point at (0, 0).

The graph of $y = x^2$ is wider than the graph of $y = 2x^2$. The graph of $y = 2x^2$ is wider than the graph of $y = 4x^2$.

Exercises

1. Make a conjecture about the graph of $y = \frac{1}{2}x^2$ as compared to the graphs above. Use the spreadsheet to graph $y = \frac{1}{2}x^2$ and verify your conjecture.

2. Graph the quadratics $y = x^2$, $y = x^2 + 2$, and $y = x^2 - 3$. What are the similarities and differences among the graphs?

13 Student Recording Sheet

Use this recording sheet with pages 174–175 of the Student Edition.

Read each question. Then fill in the correct answer.

1. Ⓐ Ⓑ Ⓒ Ⓓ

2. Ⓕ Ⓖ Ⓗ Ⓙ

3. Ⓐ Ⓑ Ⓒ Ⓓ

4. Ⓕ Ⓖ Ⓗ Ⓙ

5. Ⓐ Ⓑ Ⓒ Ⓓ

6. Record your answer and fill in the bubbles in the grid below. Be sure to use the correct place value.

7. Ⓕ Ⓖ Ⓗ Ⓙ

8. Ⓐ Ⓑ Ⓒ Ⓓ

9. Ⓕ Ⓖ Ⓗ Ⓙ

10. Ⓐ Ⓑ Ⓒ Ⓓ

11. Ⓕ Ⓖ Ⓗ Ⓙ

12. Record your answer and fill in the bubbles in the grid below. Be sure to use the correct place value.

13. Ⓐ Ⓑ Ⓒ Ⓓ

Pre-AP

Record your answers for Question 14 on the back of this paper.

Assessment

13 Rubric for Scoring Pre-AP

(Use to score the Pre-AP question on page 737 of the Student Edition.)

General Scoring Guidelines

- If a student gives only a correct numerical answer to a problem but does not show how he or she arrived at the answer, the student will be awarded only 1 credit. All extended-response questions require the student to show work.

- A fully correct answer for a multiple-part question requires correct responses for all parts of the question. For example, if a question has three parts, the correct response to one or two parts of the question that required work to be shown is *not* considered a fully correct response.

- Students who use trial and error to solve a problem must show their method. Merely showing that the answer checks or is correct is not considered a complete response for full credit.

Exercise 14 Rubric

Score	Specific Criteria
4	A correct solution that is supported by well-developed, accurate explanations. An accurate explanation that the total volume of all five posts is $(\pi \cdot 6^2 \cdot 6) + (\pi \cdot 6^2 \cdot 5) + (\pi \cdot 6^2 \cdot 4) + (\pi \cdot 6^2 \cdot 3) + (\pi \cdot 6^2 \cdot 2) = 15.7$ ft^3 is given. An accurate explanation that the sculpture weighs $(12 \cdot 15.7$ ft$^3) = 188.4$ lb is given.
3	A generally correct solution, but may contain minor flaws in reasoning or computation.
2	A partially correct interpretation and/or solution to the problem.
1	A correct solution with no supporting evidence or explanation.
0	An incorrect solution indicating no mathematical understanding of the concept or task, or no solution is given.

13 Chapter 13 Quiz 1

(Lessons 13–1 and 13–2)

Determine whether each expression is a polynomial. If it is, classify it as a *monomial*, *binomial*, or *trinomial*.

1. $r^2 + rs + 9$

1. _____

2. $\dfrac{xy}{z} - z$

2. _____

For Questions 3 and 4, find the degree of each polynomial.

3. xy

3. _____

4. $4m + n$

4. _____

5. Which type of polynomial has two unlike terms?

5. _____

Find each sum.

6. $(4m + 3) + (2m + 8)$

6. _____

7. $(6x + 2) + (x - 1)$

7. _____

8. $(9y - 4s) + (y + 7s)$

8. _____

9. $(6p^2 + 2p + 3) + (4p^2 + p + 6)$

9. _____

10. $(5x^2y - xy) + (-6x^2y)$

10. _____

---

13 Chapter 13 Quiz 2

(Lesson 13–3)

Find each difference.

1. $(8y + 6) - (3y + 9)$

1. _____

2. $(4x + 2y) - (x + y)$

2. _____

3. $(3x^2 - 2x) - (x^2 + 5x)$

3. _____

4. $(12x^2 - 2) - (x + 5)$

4. _____

5. **GEOMETRY** The perimeter of the triangle shown at the right is $7x + 2$ units. Find the length of the missing side of the triangle.

5. _____

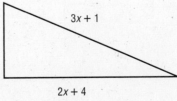

$3x + 1$

$2x + 4$

Assessment

13 Chapter 13 Quiz 3

SCORE _____

(Lessons 13–4 and 13–5)

Find each product.

1. $3a(9 + a)$

2. $-6c(c^4 - 2c^2 + 7)$

1. _____

For Questions 3 and 4, determine whether each graph or table represents a *linear* or *nonlinear* function. Explain.

2. _____

3.

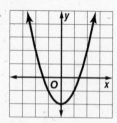

4.

x	y
-2	40
5	30
12	20
19	10

3. _____

4. _____

5. MULTIPLE CHOICE Which equation describes a linear function?

A. $a = (a + 3)5a$

C. $-4t^2 + 3r = 7$

B. $x + 9y = 15$

D. $y = 3m^3 + 1$

5. _____

- -

13 Chapter 13 Quiz 4

SCORE _____

(Lesson 13–6)

For Questions 1 and 2, graph each function.

1. $y = -x^3$

1.

2. $y = x^3 - 1$

2.

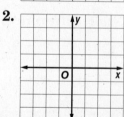

3. Graph $y = 2x^2$ and $y = x^2$ on the same coordinate plane. Describe their similarities and differences.

3.

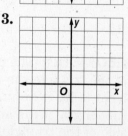

13 Chapter 13 Mid-Chapter Test

(Lessons 13–1 through 13–4)

Part I *Write the letter for the correct answer in the blank at the right of each question.*

Find the degree of each polynomial.

1. $-12xy^2$
   A. 1   **B.** 2   **C.** 3   **D.** 4   1. _____

2. $x^3 + x^2y^3 + y^6$
   F. 3   **G.** 5   **H.** 6   **J.** 14   2. _____

For Questions 3–6 find each sum or difference.

3. $(m^2 + s) + (3m^2 + ms)$
   A. $3m^2 + ms^2$ **C.** $3m^4 + ms^2$
   B. $4m^2 + ms + s$ **D.** $4m^2 + ms^2$ 3. _____

4. $(-4x^2 + x - 3) + (x^2 - 2x + 1)$
   F. $-3x^2 - x - 2$ **H.** $-5x^2 - 3x - 4$
   G. $-3x^4 - x^2 - 2$ **J.** $-4x^2 - 2$ 4. _____

5. $(3t + 4r) - (-t - r)$
   A. $4t + 5r$ **B.** $2t + 3r$ **C.** $3t + 4r$ **D.** $4t^2 + 5r^2$ 5. _____

6. $(6y^2 + 5y - 3) - (4y^2 + 5y + 4)$
   F. -5 **G.** $2y^2 + 5y - 7$ **H.** $2y^2 - 7$ **J.** $10y^2 + 1$ 6. _____

7. Choose the expression that is *not* a binomial.

   A. $3ab - 1$ **B.** $x^2 + y$ **C.** $m^3 - 2$ **D.** $\frac{1}{3}x + x$ 7. _____

Part II

Determine whether each expression is a polynomial. If it is, classify it as a *monomial*, *binomial*, or *trinomial*.

8. $0.7x^3$ 9. $\dfrac{x^2}{y} - \dfrac{2z}{w}$ 10. $\dfrac{2}{3}m + \dfrac{1}{2}n - r$

8. _____

9. _____

10. _____

Find each sum or difference.

11. $(6x + 7) + (3x + 5)$

11. _____

12. $(-3b^2 + 4b - 6) + (3b^2 - 3b - 5)$

12. _____

13. $(7x + 4) - (3x + 1)$

13. _____

14. $(4a^2 - 4b + 5) - (2a^2 + 3b - 1)$

14. _____

Assessment

13 Chapter 13 Vocabulary Test

additive inverse	degree	polynomial
binomial	linear function	quadratic function
cubic function	nonlinear function	trinomial

Write whether each sentence is *true* or *false*. If false, replace the underlined word or number to make a true sentence.

1. A <u>cubic function</u> has a degree of 3.

1. _____

2. The expression $5x^3$ is a <u>polynomial</u>.

2. _____

3. The degree of the polynomial $4x^2y^3 + xy$ is <u>3</u>.

3. _____

4. The polynomial in any equation that represents a <u>quadratic function</u> has a degree of 3.

4. _____

5. A polynomial with three terms is called a <u>binomial</u>.

5. _____

6. The constant 0 has <u>no degree</u>.

6. _____

7. A <u>quadratic function</u> has a graph that is a straight line.

7. _____

8. You can subtract a polynomial by adding its <u>reciprocal</u>.

8. _____

9. $6x^2 + 2x$ and $5x + 2$ are both examples of <u>binomials</u>.

9. _____

10. Quadratic functions and cubic functions are both examples of <u>nonlinear functions</u>.

10. _____

Define each term in your own words.

11. degree of a monomial

12. degree of a polynomial

13 **Chapter 13 Test, Form 1**

Write the letter for the correct answer in the blank at the right of each question.

1. Choose the expression that is *not* a polynomial.

   A. $6y - \dfrac{4}{y}$ **B.** $\dfrac{4x}{9} + \dfrac{2y}{5}$ **C.** $5x^2y + 7x$ **D.** $5a + 6b$ **1.** _____

2. The expression $x^2 + 2x$ is a
   F. monomial.   **G.** binomial.   **H.** trinomial.   **J.** constant.   **2.** _____

3. Find the degree of $5bc$.
   A. 0   **B.** 1   **C.** 2   **D.** 3   **3.** _____

4. Find the degree of $yx^3 + xy$.
   F. 2   **G.** 3   **H.** 4   **J.** 6   **4.** _____

Find each sum.

5. $(9f + 4) + (f + 2)$
   A. $10f - 6$ **B.** $10f + 6$ **C.** $8f + 2$ **D.** $9f^2 + 6f$ **5.** _____

6. $(2x + 2) + (x - 6)$
   F. $4x^2 - 12$ **G.** $x + 8$ **H.** $3x - 4$ **J.** $x - 8$ **6.** _____

7. $(5a + 3b) + (6a + 2b)$
   A. $11a + 5b$ **B.** $-a + b$ **C.** $11a - 5b$ **D.** $a - b$ **7.** _____

8. $(3x^2 + y) + (5x^2 - 1 + y)$
   F. $-2x^2 + 3y$ **G.** $8x^2 + y$ **H.** $-2x^2 - 3y$ **J.** $8x^2 + 2y - 1$ **8.** _____

Find each difference.

9. $(6m + 4) - (3m + 1)$
   A. $9m + 5$ **B.** $3m + 3$ **C.** $3m + 5m$ **D.** $3m - 5$ **9.** _____

10. $(7x - 5) - (2x - 1)$
    F. $5x + 4$ **G.** $9x - 4$ **H.** $5x - 4$ **J.** $5x - 4x$ **10.** _____

11. $(3a + 7b) - (a + b)$
    A. $2a + 6b$ **B.** $4a + 8b$ **C.** $2a - 6b$ **D.** $4a - 8b$ **11.** _____

12. $(4x^2 - x + 1) - (3x^2 - 2x - 8)$
    F. $7x^2 - 3x + 7$ **G.** $x^2 - 3x - 7$ **H.** $7x^2 + 3x - 9$ **J.** $x^2 + x + 9$ **12.** _____

Assessment

13 **Chapter 13 Test, Form 1** *(continued)*

Find each product.

13. $4(3y + 5)$

    A. $7y - 9$ **B.** $7y + 9$ **C.** $12y + 20$ **D.** $12y + 20y$ 13. _____

14. $b(b - 3)$

    F. $-b$ **G.** $b^2 - 3b$ **H.** $2b - 3b$ **J.** $b^2 + 3b$ 14. _____

15. $3t(t + 7)$

    A. $3t^2 + 21t$ **B.** $3t^2 - 21t^2$ **C.** $-18t^2$ **D.** $14t$ 15. _____

16. $(6x + y)x$

    F. $7x + xy$ **G.** $6x^2 + x + y$ **H.** $7x - xy$ **J.** $6x^2 + xy$ 16. _____

17. Which equation describes a nonlinear function?

    A. $x = \dfrac{y}{4}$ **B.** $x = 3x + 7$ **C.** $y = x^2y$ **D.** $y = 5(x - 1)$ 17. _____

18. Which type of function does the graph shown at the right represent?

    F. linear   **H.** cubic

    G. nonlinear   **J.** quadratic

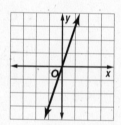

18. _____

19. Choose the graph that represents $y = x^3 + 1$.

    A. 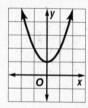   **B.** 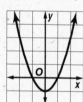   **C.** 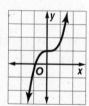   **D.** 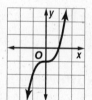   19. _____

20. Choose the equation that represents the graph at the right.

    F. $y = -x^2$ **H.** $y = x^3$

    G. $y = x^2$ **J.** $y = -x^3$

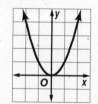

20. _____

Bonus GEOMETRY A rectangle has sides of length $3x - 4$ and width $x - y$. Find the perimeter.

    B: _____

13 **Chapter 13 Test, Form 2A**

Write the letter for the correct answer in the blank at the right of each question.

1. Choose the expression that is *not* a polynomial.

   A. $\frac{4}{9}$ **B.** $5x^2y^3 + 7x^3y^2$ **C.** $\sqrt{a - 2b}$ **D.** $6x + \frac{y}{8}$ 1. _____

2. Find the degree of $7ab^3c^5$.

   F. 9   **G.** 8   **H.** 16   **J.** 7   2. _____

3. The expression $\frac{2}{3}x + \frac{1}{2}y - z$ is a

   A. monomial.   **B.** binomial.   **C.** trinomial.   **D.** constant.   3. _____

4. Find the degree of $x^3 + x^2y^3 + y^4$.

   F. 5   **G.** 4   **H.** 3   **J.** 12   4. _____

Find each sum or difference.

5. $(9x + 2) + (6x + 4)$

   A. $3x - 2$ **B.** $15x + 6$ **C.** $15x - 6$ **D.** $3x + 2$ 5. _____

6. $(5x - 7y + 4) - (2x + y - 3)$

   F. $7x - 7y + 7$ **G.** $7x + 8y - 7$ **H.** $3x - 8y + 7$ **J.** $3x - 6y - 1$ 6. _____

7. $(6a^2 + b^2) + (-3a + b^2)$

   A. $6a^2 - 3a + 2b^2$ **C.** $9a^2 - 3a$

   B. $3a^2 + 2b^2$ **D.** $9a^3 + 2b^2$ 7. _____

8. $(7t^2 - 4s^2) - (2t^2 + 10s^2)$

   F. $9t^2 + 6s^2$ **G.** $9t^2 - 6s^2$ **H.** $5t^2 + 14s^2$ **J.** $5t^2 - 14s^2$ 8. _____

For Questions 9 and 10, refer to the rectangle.

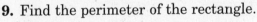

$3x - 7$

9. Find the perimeter of the rectangle.

   A. $4x^2 + 7$ **C.** $4x - 7$

   B. $8x - 14$ **D.** $3x^2 - 7$ 9. _____

10. If the perimeter of the rectangle is 34 centimeters, what is the value of x?

    F. 5   **G.** 6   **H.** 7   **J.** 8   10. _____

11. **GEOMETRY** Franklin plans to trim a piece of carpet to fit a space with an area of $2x^2 + 3x + 4$. The area of the carpet is $2x^2 + 9x + 11$. How much of the carpet will Franklin have to trim so that it will fit into the space?

    A. $4x^2 + 12x + 15$ **C.** $12x + 15$

    B. $-6x + 7$ **D.** $6x + 7$ 11. _____

Assessment

For Questions 12–15, find each product.

12. $7(3 + 4b)$

   F. $10 - 28b$ **G.** $21 + 28b$ **H.** $10 + 11b$ **J.** $49b$ 12. _____

13. $t(5t - 3)$

   A. $5t^2 + 3t$ **B.** $5t - 3t$ **C.** $5t^2 - 3t$ **D.** $5t + 3t$ 13. _____

14. $-2(4x^2 - 8x)$

   F. $-8x^2 + 16x$ **G.** $8x^2 - 16x$ **H.** $-6x^2 - 10x$ **J.** $6x^2 + 10x$ 14. _____

15. $(x + 4y)3x$

   A. $3x + 12xy$ **B.** $3x + 12y$ **C.** $3x^2 + 7xy$ **D.** $3x^2 + 12xy$ 15. _____

16. SPORTS The perimeter of a singles tennis court is 210 feet. The length is equal to 2 times the width plus 24. Find the width.

   F. 62 ft   **G.** 27 ft   **H.** 43 ft   **J.** 78 ft   16. _____

17. Which equation describes a nonlinear function?

   A. $y = 1.3x$ **B.** $y = \dfrac{4x}{7}$ **C.** $y = x^3 - 5$ **D.** $12 = 3x + 4y$ 17. _____

18. The graph shown at the right represents a function that is

   F. linear.   **H.** cubic.

   G. nonlinear.   **J.** quadratic.

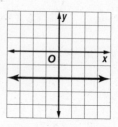

18. _____

19. Choose the graph that represents $y = 3x^3 + 1$.

   A. 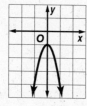   **B.** 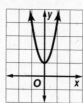   **C.** 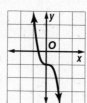   **D.** 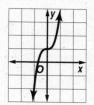   19. _____

20. Choose the equation that represents the graph shown at the right.

   F. $x^3 - 3$ **H.** $x^2 + 3$

   G. $-x^3 - 3$ **J.** $-x^2 + 3$

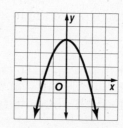

20. _____

Bonus Write a binomial with degree 4.   B: _____

13 **Chapter 13 Test, Form 2B**

Write the letter for the correct answer in the blank at the right of each question.

1. Choose the expression that is *not* a polynomial.

   A. $\frac{4}{5}$ **B.** $\frac{4}{x}$ **C.** $3x^2y - 7xy^2$ **D.** $12x - \frac{y}{7}$ 1. _____

2. Find the degree of $3ab^6$.

   F. 18   **G.** 8   **H.** 6   **J.** 7   2. _____

3. The expression $x^2 + 2x + 4$ is a

   A. monomial.   **B.** binomial.   **C.** trinomial.   **D.** constant.   3. _____

4. Find the degree of $x^2y + xy + 3y^2$.

   F. 1   **G.** 2   **H.** 3   **J.** 4   4. _____

Find each sum or difference.

5. $(7x + 3) + (6x + 5)$

   A. $x - 2$ **B.** $13x + 8$ **C.** $13x - 8$ **D.** $x + 2$ 5. _____

6. $(-x^2 - 9x + 4) - (6x^2 + 5x + 1)$

   F. $-7x^2 - 14x + 3$ **H.** $-7x^2 - 4x + 5$

   G. $-5x^2 + 4x^2 + 5$ **J.** $-5x^2 + 4x^2 + 3$ 6. _____

7. $(10a^2 + b^2) + (-4a + b^2)$

   A. $14a^2 + 2b^2$ **C.** $6a^2 + 2b^2$

   B. $10a^2 + 4a - 2b^2$ **D.** $10a^2 - 4a + 2b^2$ 7. _____

8. $(8t^2 - 5s^2) - (2t^2 + 10s^2)$

   F. $16t^2 - 15s^2$ **G.** $6t^2 - 15s^2$ **H.** $8t^2 - 2t - 15s^2$ **J.** $10t^2 + 5s^2$ 8. _____

For Questions 9 and 10, refer to the rectangle.

x

$2x + 4$

9. Find the perimeter of the rectangle.

   A. $2x^2 + 4x$ **C.** $6x + 8$

   B. $3x + 4$ **D.** $2x^2 + 4$ 9. _____

10. If the perimeter of the rectangle is 38 centimeters, what is the value of x?

   F. 5   **G.** 6   **H.** 8   **J.** 19   10. _____

11. **GEOMETRY** Marcus plans to trim a piece of carpet to fit a space with an area of $2x^2 + 5x + 4$. The area of the carpet is $2x^2 + 8x + 10$. How much of the carpet will Marcus have to trim so that it will fit into the space?

   A. $3x + 14$ **C.** $3x + 6$

   B. $4x^2 + 13x + 14$ **D.** $3x - 6$ 11. _____

Assessment

13 Chapter 13 Test, Form 2B (continued)

For Questions 12–15, find each product.

12. $6(4 + 3b)$

    F. $10 + 9b$ **G.** $24 + 18b$ **H.** $24b + 18b$ **J.** $10 - 9b$ 12. _____

13. $t(8t - 2)$

    A. $8t^2 + 2t$ **B.** $6t^2$ **C.** $8t^2 - 2t$ **D.** $8t^2 + 2t^2$ 13. _____

14. $-3(2x^2 - 5x)$

    F. $-6x^2 + 15x$ **G.** $6x^2 - 15x$ **H.** $-5x^2 + 8x$ **J.** $5x^2 - 8x$ 14. _____

15. $(x + 3y)4x$

    A. $5x^2 + 7xy$ **B.** $4x^2 + 12x$ **C.** $4x^2 + 12y$ **D.** $4x^2 + 12xy$ 15. _____

16. **SPORTS** The perimeter of a doubles tennis court is 228 feet. The length is equal to 2 times the width plus 6. Find the width of a doubles tennis court.

    F. 74 ft   **G.** 36 ft   **H.** 42 ft   **J.** 78 ft   16. _____

17. Which equation represents a nonlinear function?

    A. $y = x^3 + 1$ **B.** $y = \dfrac{3x}{8}$ **C.** $15 = 2x + 3y$ **D.** $1.7x = y$ 17. _____

18. The graph shown at the right represents a function that is

    F. linear.   **H.** cubic.

    G. nonlinear.   **J.** quadratic.   18. _____

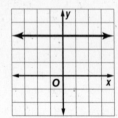

19. Choose the graph that represents $y = x^2 - 1$.

    A. 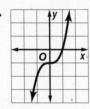   **B.** 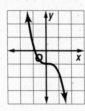   **C.** 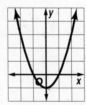   **D.** 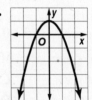   19. _____

20. Choose the equation that represents the graph shown at the right.

    F. $y = -x^2 - 2$ **H.** $y = -x^3 + 2$

    G. $y = x^2 + 2$ **J.** $y = x^3 - 2$ 20. _____

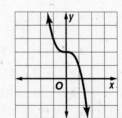

Bonus Write a trinomial with degree 5.   **B:** _____

13 **Chapter 13 Test, Form 2C**

Determine whether each expression is a polynomial. If it is, classify it as a *monomial*, *binomial*, or *trinomial*.

1. $3 + x + x^2$

1. _____

2. $\frac{x}{3}$

2. _____

ART For Questions 3 and 4, refer to the diagram of a stained glass window at the right.

3. Write a polynomial that represents the perimeter of the stained glass window.

3. _____

4. What is the degree of the polynomial?

4. _____

Find each sum or difference.

5. $(2x + 4) + (3x + 3)$

5. _____

6. $(8y + 7) - (4y + 3)$

6. _____

7. $(5a^2 + b^2) + (-3a + b^2)$

7. _____

8. $(7t^2 - 5s^2) - (4t^2 + 10s^2)$

8. _____

9. $(6x^2 + 5x + 2) - (x^2 + 2x + 4)$

9. _____

GEOMETRY For Questions 10–12, refer to the rectangle at the right.

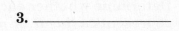

10. Find the perimeter of the rectangle.

10. _____

11. If the perimeter of the rectangle is 46 centimeters, what is the value of x?

11. _____

12. Find the dimensions of the rectangle.

12. _____

For Questions 13–18, find each product.

13. $3(4x + 1)$

13. _____

14. $-b(5b + 2)$

14. _____

15. $(6 + 3y)y$

15. _____

16. $(9 + 3a)4a$

16. _____

17. $-4c(4c - 1)$

17. _____

18. $km(k^2 - 2)$

18. _____

55

Assessment

19. **SPORTS** The dimensions of a singles badminton court are different from the dimensions of a singles tennis court, as shown in the table. Use the information in the table to find the length and width of each court.

Measure (feet)	Tennis	Badminton
Perimeter	210	122
Width	x	y
Length	$2(x + 12)$	$2(y + 5)$

19. _____

Determine whether each graph, equation, or table represents a *linear* or *nonlinear* function. Explain.

20.

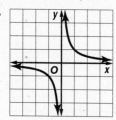

21.

x	y
3	40
7	30
11	20
15	10

22. $ab = 12$

20. _____

21. _____

22. _____

For Questions 23 and 24, graph each function.

23. $y = 3x^2$

23.

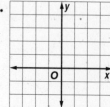

24. $y = x^3 + 2$

24.

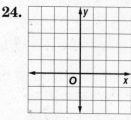

25. Graph $y = x^3 - 3$ and $y = 3x^3$. Are these equations functions? Explain.

25.

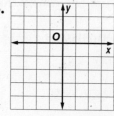

_____

Bonus Find two polynomials with a difference that is $2x^2 + x + 4$. **B:** _____

13 Chapter 13 Test, Form 2D

Determine whether each expression is a polynomial. If it is, classify it as a *monomial*, *binomial*, or *trinomial*.

1. $\frac{3}{x}$ 2. $x^2 + x + 2$

1. _____

2. _____

ART For Questions 3 and 4, refer to the diagram of a stained glass window at the right.

3. Write a polynomial that represents the perimeter of the stained glass window.

4. What is the degree of the polynomial?

3. _____

4. _____

Find each sum or difference.

5. $(3x + 2) + (5x + 3)$

6. $(9y + 7) - (4y + 3)$

7. $(4a^2 + b^2) + (-2a + b^2)$

8. $(6t^2 - 7s^2) - (3t^2 + 10s^2)$

9. $(5x^2 + 7x + 3) - (2x^2 + x + 7)$

5. _____

6. _____

7. _____

8. _____

9. _____

GEOMETRY For Questions 10–12, refer to the rectangle at the right.

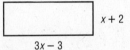 $x + 2$

$3x - 3$

10. Find the perimeter of the rectangle.

11. If the perimeter of the rectangle is 38 centimeters, what is the value of x?

12. Find the dimensions of the rectangle.

10. _____

11. _____

12. _____

For Questions 13–18, find each product.

13. $4(5x - 2)$

14. $-b(6b + 1)$

15. $(7 + 2y)y$

16. $(7 + 2a)5a$

17. $-3c(5c - 2)$

18. $km(k^3 + 4)$

13. _____

14. _____

15. _____

16. _____

17. _____

18. _____

19. **SPORTS** The perimeter of a singles tennis court is different from the perimeter of a doubles tennis court, as shown in the table. Use the information in the table to find the length and width of each court.

19. _____

Measure (feet)	Singles	Doubles
Perimeter	210	228
Width	y	x
Length	$2(y + 12)$	$2(x + 3)$

Determine whether each graph, equation, or table represents a *linear* or *nonlinear* function. Explain.

20.

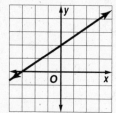

21.

x	y
11	1
9	2
6	3
4	4

22. $y = \dfrac{x}{4}$

20. _____

21. _____

22. _____

For Questions 23 and 24, graph each function.

23. $y = 2x^2$

23.

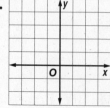

24. $y = x^3 - 1$

24.

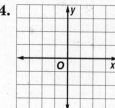

25. Graph $y = x^2 - 1$ and $y = -x^2$. Are these equations functions? Explain.

25.

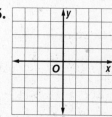

_____

Bonus GEOMETRY Find the area of a rectangle with width $4x$ cm and length $2x^2 - 9x + 4$ cm.

B: _____

13 **Chapter 13 Test, Form 3**

Determine whether each expression is a polynomial. If it is, classify it as a *monomial*, *binomial*, or *trinomial*.

1. $\sqrt{3x^2 - 2y}$ 2. $7w^3 + \frac{1}{3}x^2 + \frac{1}{2}$

1. _____

2. _____

Tell whether each statement is *always*, *sometimes*, or *never* true. Explain.

3. A binomial has a degree of 2.

3. _____

4. A trinomial has 3 terms.

4. _____

Find each sum or difference.

5. $(7x + 3) + (4x - 5)$

5. _____

6. $(7k - 6) - (2k - 4)$

6. _____

7. $(3z^2 + 5zw + 3w^2) + (4z^2 - 2w^2)$

7. _____

8. $(4x^2 - 5xy + 3y^2) - (2x^2 - 4xy + 5y^2)$

8. _____

9. $(-6x^2 + x - 7) - (x^2 - 4x - 5)$

9. _____

Find each sum. Then evaluate if $a = -2$, $b = 3$ and $c = 5$.

10. $(2b + 3a) + (4b - 7a)$

10. _____

11. $(a^2 + 6b^2) + (9 - 3b^2) + (2a^2 - 10)$

11. _____

12. $(4a + 6b - 3c) + (a - 4b + 7c) + (-2a + 2b + c)$

12. _____

For Questions 13–18, find each product.

13. $x(x - 7)$

13. _____

14. $(y^2 - 2)6y$

14. _____

15. $-rs(r^2 + 5)$

15. _____

16. $(-3x^2 + 2x - 11)4$

16. _____

17. $-2m(7 - 4m + 3m^2)$

17. _____

18. $5b(b^3 + 9b - 4)$

18. _____

19. Solve $8a - 12 = -6(a - 5)$.

19. _____

Assessment

For Questions 20 and 21, determine whether each graph, equation, or table represents a *linear* or *nonlinear* function. Explain.

20.

x	y
−11	18
−8	13
−5	8
−2	3

21.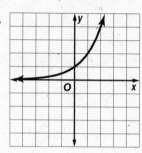

20. _____

21. _____

22. $y = \dfrac{6}{x-1}$

22. _____

Graph each function.

23. $y = \dfrac{1}{2}x^2 - 1$

23.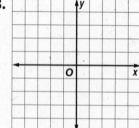

24. $y = \dfrac{1}{3}x^3 + 1$

24.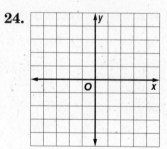

25. Write the function for the volume V of a rectangular prism as a function of a fixed height of 4 and a square base of varying lengths s. Then graph.

25. _____

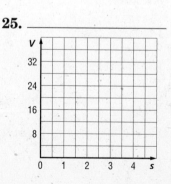

Bonus A rectangle is 9 feet longer than it is wide. If the rectangle has a perimeter of 326 feet, how long is each side?

B: _____

13 Chapter 13 Extended-Response Test

Demonstrate your knowledge by giving a clear, concise solution to each problem. Be sure to include all relevant drawings and justify your answers. You may show your solution in more than one way or investigate beyond the requirements of the problem.

1. An algebraic expression that contains one or more monomials is called a polynomial.

   a. Complete the table below.

Sample Polynomial	Number of Terms	Type of Polynomial	Degree of Polynomial
$\frac{3}{5}x^4$	1		
$3r^3 - r^2$			3
$a^2 + 2ab + b^2$			
$x^4y^3 + 4x^3y - 15xy^2$			

   b. Write a trinomial that contains only one variable.

   c. Write a monomial that contains exactly three variables.

   d. Explain how your answers to parts b and c differ.

2. Tiles can be used to model polynomials.

   a. Draw tiles to represent $3x^2 + 2x - 4$.

   b. Draw tiles to find the sum $(2x^2 + x + 3) + (x^2 - 3x + 2)$. Explain each step.

   c. Find two polynomials with a difference that is $2x^2 - x + 3$. Draw tiles to demonstrate finding their difference.

3. Refer to the table at the right.

   a. Graph the ordered pairs in the table.

   b. Sketch a line or curve through the points.

   c. Does your graph represent a *linear* or a *nonlinear* function? Explain.

   d. Write a function that includes all of the ordered pairs in the table.

x	y
−2	−7
−1	0
0	1
1	2
2	9

Assessment

13 **Standardized Test Practice**

(Chapters 1–13)

Part 1: Multiple Choice
Instructions: Fill in the appropriate circle for the best answer.

1. The area of a rectangle is 90 square meters. Its width is 15 meters. Find the perimeter. (Lesson 3–8)

   A 21 m   **B** 28 m   **C** 42 m   **D** 210 m   1. Ⓐ Ⓑ Ⓒ Ⓓ

2. Find the quotient of $3\frac{3}{4}$ and $\frac{5}{7}$. (Lesson 5–4)

   F $5\frac{1}{4}$ **G** $3\frac{1}{28}$ **H** $2\frac{2}{3}$ **J** $\frac{4}{21}$ 2. Ⓕ Ⓖ Ⓗ Ⓙ

3. A discount shopping club sells a set of 4 books for $9.99. Individually, each book sells for $3.95. What is the percent of discount on each book? (Lesson 6–8)

   A 25%   **B** 37%   **C** 42%   **D** 58%   3. Ⓐ Ⓑ Ⓒ Ⓓ

4. Find the slope of the line. (Lesson 7–5)

   F 4   **H** $-\frac{1}{4}$

   G $\frac{1}{4}$ **J** -4

   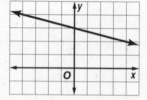

   4. Ⓕ Ⓖ Ⓗ Ⓙ

5. Find the value of *x* to the nearest tenth. (Lesson 9–4)

   A 3.3 cm   **C** 14.5 cm

   B 4.4 cm   **D** 15.5 cm

   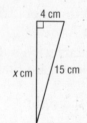

   5. Ⓐ Ⓑ Ⓒ Ⓓ

6. Mrs. Sato is putting a fence around her circular flower garden. The garden is 6 feet across the center. How long is the fence? (Lesson 10–7)

   F 6 ft   **G** 9.42 ft   **H** 18.85 ft   **J** 36.78 ft   6. Ⓕ Ⓖ Ⓗ Ⓙ

7. Find the slant height of a square pyramid with a base side length of 5 cm and a surface area of 120 cm. (Lesson 11–5)

   A 12 cm   **B** 11.7 cm   **C** 9.5 cm   **D** 5.4 cm   7. Ⓐ Ⓑ Ⓒ Ⓓ

8. The histogram shows the ages of the students in the Japanese exchange program. What is the total number of students involved in the exchange? (Lesson 12–4)

   F 20   **H** 24

   G 22   **J** 26

   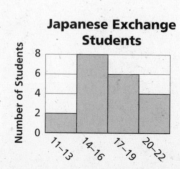

   8. Ⓕ Ⓖ Ⓗ Ⓙ

13 Standardized Test Practice *(continued)*

9. One bag contains two red and four white beads. Another bag contains three green and four black beads. One bead is drawn from each bag. Find P(white and black). (Lesson 12–10)

   A $\frac{16}{21}$ **B** $\frac{8}{21}$ **C** $\frac{8}{42}$ **D** $\frac{2}{13}$ 9. Ⓐ Ⓑ Ⓒ Ⓓ

10. Find the sum $(3a - 6b + c) + (2a + 6b - 4c)$. (Lesson 13–2)

    F $6a - 4$ **G** $5a + 5c$ **H** $5a - 3c$ **J** $5a + 12b$ 10. Ⓕ Ⓖ Ⓗ Ⓙ

11. Find the difference $(8m + 6) - (-2m - 4)$. (Lesson 13–3)

    A $6m - 2$ **B** $6m + 2$ **C** $10m + 2$ **D** $10m + 10$ 11. Ⓐ Ⓑ Ⓒ Ⓓ

12. Find the product $-3x(3x - 2)$. (Lesson 13–4)

    F $-9x^2 + 6$ **G** $-9x^2 - 6x$ **H** $-9x^2 + 6x$ **J** $-9x^2 - 6$ 12. Ⓕ Ⓖ Ⓗ Ⓙ

13. Which equation represents a linear function? (Lesson 13–5)

    A $4xy = 15$ **B** $y = \frac{1}{3}x$ **C** $x^3 - 1 = y$ **D** $y = x(x + 7)$ 13. Ⓐ Ⓑ Ⓒ Ⓓ

14. Find the slope of the line through the points $(2,4)$ and $(3, -6)$. (Lesson 7-5)

    F 10 **G** $-\frac{5}{2}$ **H** -10 **J** $-\frac{1}{10}$ 14. Ⓕ Ⓖ Ⓗ Ⓙ

15. Find the median of the following set of data 25, 15, 7, 17, 10, 30. (Lesson 12-9)

    A 17 **B** 16 **C** 12 **D** 7 15. Ⓐ Ⓑ Ⓒ Ⓓ

16. Find the degree of $12x^2 + 8x - 6$. (Lesson 13-1)

    F 1 **G** 2 **H** 3 **J** 4 16. Ⓕ Ⓖ Ⓗ Ⓙ

Part 2: Griddable

Instructions: Enter your answer by writing each digit of the answer in a column box and then shading in the appropriate circle that corresponds to that entry.

17. The dimensions of a rectangular prism are: height 2.9 m, width 1.4 m, and length 3.01 m. Find the volume of the prism in cubic meters. Round to the nearest tenth. (Lesson 11–2)

18. Find the degree of $13x^3 + xy - 0.5y^2$. (Lesson 13–1)

Assessment

13 Standardized Test Practice (continued)

Part 3: Short Response

Instructions: Write your answer in the blank at the right of each question.

19. Michael drops three quarters. What are the odds they will all land heads up? If he drops the quarters 100 times, about how many times should they land heads up? (Lesson 12–8)

   19. _____

20. Write an equation to represent the volume V of a cone with height $\frac{12}{\pi}$ and radius r. Is this equation a function? (Lesson 13–6)

   20. _____

21. Find the value of $\frac{3[4(5+2)]}{12}$. (Lesson 1–2)

   21. _____

22. Wei-Ling wants to start a lawn in an area that is 110 feet by 70 feet. One bag of seed covers 1200 square feet. How many bags should he buy? (Lesson 3–8)

   22. _____

23. Write 2,850,000,000 in scientific notation. (Lesson 4–7)

   23. _____

24. Find the slope of a line that passes through the points $A(-2, 6)$ and $B(5, -1)$. (Lesson 7–5)

   24. _____

25. Write the equation of the line that passes through the points $C(-2, 1)$ and $D(-1, 4)$. (Lesson 7–6)

   25. _____

26. Find the value of x. Then find the missing angle measures. (Lesson 10–4)

   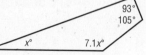

   26. _____

27. Find the surface area of a cone with radius 7 centimeters and a slant height 10.5 centimeters. If necessary, round to the nearest tenth. (Lesson 11–5)

   27. _____

28. Find the missing measure for the pair of similar solids. (Lesson 11–6)

   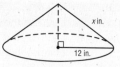

   28. _____

29. Find the product of $-3x(-5x + 3)$. (Lesson 13–4)

   29. _____

30. Colin has a choice of ham, turkey, or roast beef sandwich on white, wheat, or sourdough bread and a choice of an apple, banana, or orange. (Lesson 12–8)

   a. How many lunches are possible if he selects a sandwich and fruit?

   30a. _____

   b. If Colin is allergic to wheat bread, how many lunches are possible?

   30b. _____

   c. If Colin also has the choice of milk or chocolate milk to drink, how many lunches are possible?

   30c. _____

Unit 5 Test

(Chapters 12–13)

For Questions 1–5, use the stem-and-leaf plot, which shows the ages of members of a community chorus.

Stem	Leaf
2	4 5 7 7 9
3	3 3 7 8 8 8 8 9
4	2 5 5 8 8 8 9 9 9
5	0 0 3 4 4 5 6 6 7 9 9
6	0 0 1 1 1 3 5 5

$2 \mid 4 = 24$

1. How old is the oldest member of the chorus?

   1. _____

2. In which interval do most of the ages occur?

   2. _____

3. What is the median age of the members?

   3. _____

4. Make a box-and-whisker plot of the data.

   4.
   20 30 40 50 60 70

5. Find the interquartile range.

   5. _____

For Questions 6 and 7, use the data in the table.

6. Display the set of data in a histogram.

Books Read Over Summer		
Books	**Tally**	**Frequency**
0–4	IIII II	7
5–9	IIII IIII IIII	14
10–14	IIII	5
15–19	III	3

6.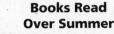

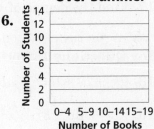

Books Read Over Summer

7. How many students read at least 5 books?

   7. _____

8. Which graph appears to show a greater increase in the price of one share of XYZ stock? Explain.

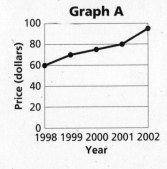

Graph A

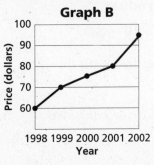

Graph B

   8. _____

9. A sheet set is available in red, green, purple, or blue and a choice of twin, queen, or king size. Find the number of different sheet sets you can buy.

   9. _____

10. Three coins are tossed. What is the probability of two tails and one head?

   10. _____

Unit 5 Test *(continued)*

(Chapters 12–13)

For Questions 11 and 12, tell whether each situation is a *permutation* or *combination*. Then solve.

11. Steve has 9 mystery books. How many ways can he arrange them on a bookshelf?

11. _____

12. How many ways can you choose 4 pair of socks out of 12 pair for a trip?

12. _____

13. Two number cubes are rolled. What is the probability of getting a sum less than 7?

13. _____

14. Danielle has 3 dimes, 2 quarters, and 5 nickels in her pocket. What is the probability that she chooses a dime followed by a quarter?

14. _____

15. An eight-sided die is rolled, find P(5 or even).

15. _____

16. Determine whether $\frac{1}{2}x + xy$ is a polynomial. If it is, classify it as a *monomial*, *binomial*, or *trinomial*.

16. _____

17. Find the degree of $xy + 3x^2y - 9$.

17. _____

For Questions 18 and 19, find each sum or difference.

18. $(a^2 + b) + (5a^2 + ab)$

18. _____

19. $(3x^2 + 6x - 3) - (x^2 + 8x + 7)$

19. _____

20. The perimeter of the triangle is $7x + 2y$ centimeters. Find the length of the third side.

$x + y$ cm $3x - y$ cm

20. _____

For Questions 21 and 22, find each product.

21. _____

21. $x(3x - 1)$ 22. $-4a(10 - 2a)$

22. _____

23. Find the perimeter of a square with side length $2x - y$ centimeters.

23. _____

24. Determine whether $y = 0.4x^2$ is a *linear* or *nonlinear* equation. Explain.

24. _____

25. Graph $y = -2x^3 + 1$.

25.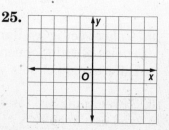

Answers (Anticipation Guide and Lesson 13-1)

13-1 Lesson Reading Guide

Polynomials

NAME _____ DATE _____ PERIOD _____

Get Ready for the Lesson

Read the introduction to Lesson 13-1 in your textbook. **Write your answers below.**

a. How many terms are in the expression for the heat index? **9**

b. What separates the terms of the expression? **plus and minus signs**

Read the Lesson **1–4. See students' work.**

Write a definition and give an example of each new vocabulary phrase.

Vocabulary	Definition	Example
1. polynomial		
2. binomial		
3. trinomial		
4. degree		

Remember What You Learned

5. Notice that the words *binomial*, *trinomial*, and *polynomial* contain the same root—*nomial*, but have different prefixes.

  a. Find the definition of the prefix *bi-* in a dictionary. Write the definition. Explain how it can help you remember the meaning of *binomial*. **Two; a binomial contains two terms.**

  b. Find the definition of the prefix *tri-* in a dictionary. Write the definition. Explain how it can help you remember the meaning of *trinomial*. **Three; a trinomial contains three terms.**

  c. Find the definition of the prefix *poly-* in a dictionary. Write the definition. Explain how it can help you remember the meaning of *polynomial*. **Many; a polynomial contains many terms.**

---

13 Anticipation Guide

Equations

NAME _____ DATE _____ PERIOD _____

Step 1 *Before you begin Chapter 13*

- Read each statement.
- Decide whether you Agree (A) or Disagree (D) with the statement.
- Write A or D in the first column OR if you are not sure whether you agree or disagree, write NS (Not Sure).

STEP 1 A, D, or NS	Statement	Step 2 A or D
	1. A trinomial is a polynomial with three terms.	A
	2. All polynomials are also binomials.	D
	3. The expression $x^2 + \dfrac{1}{x}$ is not a polynomial because it has a variable in the denominator.	A
	4. The degree of a polynomial is found by counting the number of terms.	D
	5. $8a$ and $7c$ are called like terms because both contain variables to the first power.	D
	6. To add two polynomials, add all like terms together.	A
	7. $-1(3x + 4)$ is equivalent to $-3 + 4$.	D
	8. In the expression $4t(2t^2 - 5)$, the Distributive Property can not be used because the variable t is raised to two different powers.	D
	9. A function whose graph is a curve is a nonlinear function.	A
	10. To graph the function $y = 6x^2$, make a table of values, plot the ordered pairs, and connect the points with a curve.	A

Step 2 *After you complete Chapter 13*

- Reread each statement and complete the last column by entering an A (Agree) or a D (Disagree).
- Did any of your opinions about the statements change from the first column?
- For those statements that you mark with a D, use a separate sheet of paper to explain why you disagree. Use examples, if possible.

13-1 Skills Practice

Polynomials

Determine whether each expression is a polynomial. If it is, classify it as a *monomial, binomial,* or *trinomial.*

1. $-5g^8$ — yes; monomial
2. $x + 2y + z$ — yes; trinomial
3. $5x + 1 + \frac{4}{x}$ — no
4. $r^2 - 9r$ — yes; binomial
5. $d + 1$ — yes; binomial
6. $a^3b^2 + a^2$ — yes; binomial
7. n — yes; monomial
8. $17 - \sqrt{c}$ — no
9. $a + b^2 - 3$ — yes; trinomial
10. $m + 2\sqrt{m}$ — no
11. $5y^2 - 3y + 1$ — yes; trinomial
12. $a - b + c$ — yes; trinomial
13. $24x^3$ — yes; monomial
14. $25 - 9h^4$ — yes; binomial
15. $u^5 + u^3 + u$ — yes; trinomial
16. $\frac{3x^3}{4} + \frac{x}{2} + \frac{1}{8}$ — yes; trinomial
17. $\frac{x}{5} + \frac{1}{2}$ — yes; binomial
18. $\frac{6}{a^2} - \frac{1}{a} + \frac{1}{3}$ — no
19. 1 — yes; monomial
20. $9y - \sqrt{5}$ — yes; binomial
21. $21g^5h^2$ — yes; monomial

Find the degree of each polynomial.

22. 14 — 0
23. ab — 2
24. b — 1
25. $c^3 + c^2 + c + 1$ — 3
26. mn^5 — 6
27. $xy^3z + 1$ — 5
28. $k - 4$ — 1
29. $-\frac{5}{6}$ — 0
30. 9.7 — 0
31. $c^6de^3 + c^5 + d$ — 10
32. $a^2 - 2a + 3$ — 2
33. $k^3 + 3k^4$ — 4
34. $xy^2 + 4x^2y + y^2$ — 3
35. $7b^5 - 10$ — 5
36. $16g + 3$ — 1
37. $8y^2 + 8y - 5$ — 2
38. $abc + 2ab + 5c - bc + 1$ — 3
39. $-4g^2h^5 + 2gh^4 + 9$ — 7

13-1 Study Guide and Intervention

Polynomials

Classify Polynomials Polynomials are classified according to the number of terms they have. A *monomial* has one term, a *binomial* has two terms, and a *trinomial* has three terms. The exponent of a variable in a monomial must be a whole number, and the variable cannot be in the denominator or under a radical sign.

Example 1 Determine whether each expression is a polynomial. If it is, classify it as a *monomial, binomial,* or *trinomial.*

a. $2y + \frac{3}{y}$

The expression is not a polynomial because $\frac{3}{y}$ has a variable in the denominator.

b. $\frac{3a}{4} + 6a^3 - 5a^4$

The expression is a polynomial with three terms, so it is a trinomial.

Degree of Polynomials A polynomial also has a degree. The degree of a polynomial is the same as that of the term with the greatest degree. The degree of a term is the sum of the exponents of its variables.

Example 2 Find the degree of each polynomial.

a. $x^6 - 3x^4 + 1$

The greatest degree is 6, so the degree of the trinomial is 6.

b. $10b^2c + 8bc - c^2$

$10b^2c$ has degree $2 + 1$ or 3. $8bc$ has degree $1 + 1$ or 2. c^2 has degree 2. The greatest degree is 3, so the trinomial has degree 3.

Exercises

Determine whether each expression is a polynomial. If it is, classify it as a *monomial, binomial,* or *trinomial.*

1. $7q + r - 10$ — yes; trinomial
2. $\sqrt{8r}$ — no
3. $x^2 - 4$ — yes; binomial
4. -89 — yes; monomial
5. $3v^2 + 4w$ — yes; binomial
6. $a^5 + b^2 + c$ — yes; trinomial

Find the degree of each polynomial.

7. $28y$ — 1
8. $-5h$ — 1
9. $2x^3y$ — 4
10. $9p^3 - 6p^2$ — 3
11. $mn^5 + mn^4 + m^2$ — 6
12. $8x^2 + 4xy - y^2$ — 2

13-1 Word Problem Practice

Polynomials

NAME _____ DATE _____ PERIOD _____

1. **PLANETS** The diameter of a planet can be found by knowing the distance from the viewer to the planet, d, and the planet's angular size, A, or how big it appears to be. The approximate diameter is found using the expression $\frac{2\pi}{360}\,dA$. Is this expression a polynomial? Explain. If it is, classify it as *monomial*, *binomial*, or *trinomial*.

polynomial; there are no variables in the denominator or under a radical. Monomial; it has one term.

2. **AIRPLANES** The steady ascent of an airplane is represented by the equation $y = \frac{3}{7}x + 2$. What is the degree of the polynomial? **1**

3. **BASKETBALL** A basketball player takes a shot from inside the foul line. The ball travels on an arch according to the equation $y = -0.6x^2 + 3.2x + 6$. Classify the equation as *monomial*, *binomial*, or *trinomial* and find the degree of the polynomial. **trinomial; 2**

4. **DIVING** A diver practices for an upcoming meet. She dives from a platform and follows a trajectory that can be expressed by the equation $y = 2x^4 + 12x$. Classify the equation as *monomial*, *binomial*, or *trinomial* and find the degree of the polynomial. **binomial; 4**

ROCK CLIMBING For Exercises 5–7, use the following information.

A rock climber plans to climb up one side of the mountain and down the other.

5. Write the polynomial expression that represents the distance the rock climber will travel. $\frac{2}{3}xy + 8x + 8y$

6. Classify the polynomial as a *monomial*, *binomial*, or *trinomial*. **trinomial**

7. What is the degree of the polynomial? **2**

13-1 Practice

Polynomials

NAME _____ DATE _____ PERIOD _____

Determine whether each expression is a polynomial. If it is, classify it as a *monomial*, *binomial*, or *trinomial*.

1. $-3n^2$
yes; monomial

2. $v^2 - 9v$
yes; binomial

3. $g + 2h + jk$
yes; trinomial

4. $6b + 2 + \frac{8}{b}$
no

5. $m + 10$
yes; binomial

6. $a^2b^2 + 9$
yes; binomial

7. $1 + \sqrt{s}$
no

8. q
yes; monomial

9. $h + h^2 + 1$
yes; trinomial

10. $m + n - p$
yes; trinomial

11. $y^4 + 5y - 2$
yes; trinomial

12. $x - \sqrt{x}$
no

13. $-5w^7t$
yes; monomial

14. $41 - qr^4$
yes; binomial

15. $p^4 + p^2 + p$
yes; trinomial

16. $\frac{2x^2}{7} + \frac{5x}{7} + \frac{3}{7}$
yes; trinomial

17. $\frac{v}{5} + \frac{1}{2}$
yes; binomial

18. $10k - \sqrt{6}$
yes; binomial

19. 4
yes; monomial

20. $\frac{3}{c^2} - \frac{5}{c} - \frac{1}{2}$
no

21. $7g^2h^7$
yes; monomial

Find the degree of each polynomial.

22. -52
0

23. xy
2

24. c
1

25. $2c^5 - c^3 - c - 9$
5

26. ab^3
4

27. $2cy^4z^3 + 7$
8

28. $r - 25$
1

29. $\frac{-4}{9}$
0

30. 12.4
0

31. $12 + 9t - t^2$
2

32. $5a^3 - a + 8$
3

33. $1 - c^2 + c^4$
4

34. $xy^2 - 3x^2y + xy$
3

35. $b^5 + b - 1.5$
5

36. $15k + 2$
1

37. $cde^8 + c^4 + 2e$
10

38. $wxyz - 2wx - 5y - yz + 4$
4

39. $-6g^2h^8 + gh^5 + 3$
10

40. **METEOROLOGY** *Summer simmer index* measures the discomfort level due to temperature and humidity. Meteorologists calculate this value by using a polynomial similar to $1.98x^2 - 115.93x + 0.01xy - 0.63y + 6.33$. The variable x is the temperature in °F and y is the relative humidity expressed as a whole number. What is the degree of the polynomial? **2**

NAME _____ DATE _____ PERIOD _____

13-2 Lesson Reading Guide

Adding Polynomials

Get Ready for the Lesson

Read the introduction to Lesson 13-2 in your textbook. Write your answers below.

a. Write the polynomial for the tiles that remain. $x^2 - 2x + 2$

b. Find the sum of $x^2 + 4x + 2$ and $7x^2 - 2x + 3$ by using algebra tiles.
$8x^2 + 2x + 5$

c. Compare and contrast finding the sums of polynomials with finding the sum of integers.
The concept of the zero pairs is the same, but there are tiles that represent different terms in polynomials.

Read the Lesson

1. Draw a model that shows $(x^2 - 4x + 2) + (2x^2 + 2x - 3)$. Write the polynomial that shows the sum. $3x^2 - 2x - 1$

2. Show how to find the sum $(5x - 2) + (4x + 4)$ both vertically and horizontally.

Vertically

$$5x - 2$$
$$(+)4x + 4$$
$$\overline{9x + 2}$$

Horizontally

$$(5x - 2) + (4x + 4)$$
$$= (5x + 4x) + (-2 + 4)$$
$$= 9x + 2$$

Remember What You Learned

3. You have learned that you can combine like terms. On the left below, write three pairs of monomials that have like terms. On the right below, write three pairs of monomials that have unlike terms. Explain your answers. **Sample answers are given.**

Like Terms	Unlike Terms
1. 23a and 12a	1. $2xy$ and $2x$
2. $4b^2c$ and b^2c	2. $3mm^2$ and $3m^2n$
3. xy^3 and $2xy^3$	3. $-8ab^3$ and $5ab^2$

NAME _____ DATE _____ PERIOD _____

13-1 Enrichment

A Cross-Number Puzzle

Use the clues at the bottom of the page to complete the puzzle. Write one digit in each box.

A 2	1	B 1	2	C 3	D 5	E 3	F 5
4		3			G 6	9	0
J 6	5	K 2	5	8	H 3	1	L 2
	9	6	3		N 1		0
O 6	3	M 7	5	P 3	Q 4	R 8	5
T 2	0		U 3	2	V 4	8	W 6
							S 1

Across

A $x^2 - 4$ for $x = 5$

B $3xy^2$ for $x = 4$ and $y = -1$

C $(2x + 50) + (x - 15)$ for $x = 0$

E $x^2 - 4x - y^2$ for $x = 10$ and $y = 5$

G x^2y for $x = 3$ and $y = 7$

I $10w + 5y$ for $w = 6$ and $y = 1$

K $3x^2 + 5x + 8$ for $x = -10$

L $(y - 8) + (10 - 4y)$ for $y = -6$

M $23x - 16x$ for $x = 11$

O $7x + 100y$ for $x = 5$ and $y = 6$

Q $(6x^2 - 2) + (4x^2 - 3)$ for $x = -7$

T $(x^2 - x + 7) + (x^2 - 2)$ for $x = 3$

U x^2y for $x = -2$ and $y = 8$

V $7y - 12y - 2$ for $y = -10$

W $w^2 - w - 7$ for $w = 9$

Down

A $(6x^2 - 1) + (4x^2 - 3)$ for $x = 5$

B $7y + 8y - 2$ for $y = 1$

D $x + x^2y^2$ for $x = 7$ and $y = 1$

F $5(7w + 3w)$ for $w = 10$

H $(z^2 + 2z + 1) + (z^2 - 2z - 2)$ for $z = 4$

J $6xy^2 - xy + 60$ for $x = 10$ and $y = 10$

K $w^2 - w - 3$ for $w = 6$

L $(3y - 20) + (45 - 3y)$ for $y = 16$

M $11x^2 - 8x^2$ for $x = -5$

N $x^2 - 2x + y^2$ for $x = 10$ and $y = 8$

P $(2x + 52) + (x - 11)$ for $x = -3$

R $2x^2 - 5x - 140$ for $x = 12$

S $(y - 75) + (120 + 4y)$ for $y = -6$

Left Page

13-2 Study Guide and Intervention
Adding Polynomials

Add Polynomials Add polynomials by combining like terms, which are monomials that contain the same variables to the same power.

Example Find $(8x^2 - 7x + 1) + (x^2 + 5)$.

Method 1 Add vertically.

$$\begin{aligned} 8x^2 - 7x + 1 \\ (+)\, x^2 \quad\;\; + 5 \\ \hline 9x^2 - 7x + 6 \end{aligned}$$

Method 2 Add horizontally.

$(8x^2 - 7x + 1) + (x^2 + 5)$
$= (8x^2 + x^2) - 7x + (1 + 5)$
$= 9x^2 - 7x + 6$

Exercises

Find each sum.

1.
$$\begin{aligned} 3x - 7 \\ (+)\, x + 1 \\ \hline 4x - 6 \end{aligned}$$

2.
$$\begin{aligned} 6d + 3 \\ (+)\, -4d + 1 \\ \hline 2d + 9 \end{aligned}$$

3.
$$\begin{aligned} 4w^2 - 6w + 3 \\ (+)\, w^2 \quad\;\; - 5 \\ \hline 5w^2 - 6w - 2 \end{aligned}$$

4.
$$\begin{aligned} 5a^2 - a \\ (+)\quad 2a - 5 \\ \hline 5a^2 + a - 5 \end{aligned}$$

5. $(-m + 3) + (7m - 1)$
$6m + 2$

6. $(9x^2 + 3x - 1) + (4x + 1)$
$9x^2 + 7x$

7. $(2k^2 - k) + (k - 1)$
$2k^2 - 1$

8. $(5a^2 + 6ab) + (-ab + b^2)$
$5a^2 + 5ab + b^2$

9. $(4c^2 - 7) + (c^2 - 3c + 6)$
$5c^2 - 3c - 1$

10. $(x^2 + y) + (xy + y)$
$x^2 + xy + 2y$

11. $(12h - 6) + (h^2 - 8h + 6)$
$h^2 + 4h$

12. $(10x^2 + x + 5) + (x - 10x^2)$
$2x + 5$

13. $(6y^2 - y + 1) + (y^2 - 3y - 6)$
$7y^2 - 4y - 5$

14. $(p^3 + 4) + (2p^2 - 2p + 3)$
$p^3 + 2p^2 - 2p + 7$

15. $(3g^2 + 3g + 5) + (5g^2 - 3)$
$8g^2 + 3g + 2$

16. $(5r^2 - 6) + (-r^2 - 4r + 7)$
$4r^2 - 4r + 1$

Right Page

13-2 Skills Practice
Adding Polynomials

Find each sum.

1.
$$\begin{aligned} 5q + 7 \\ (+)\, 2q - 2 \\ \hline 7q + 5 \end{aligned}$$

2.
$$\begin{aligned} 7f - 10 \\ (+)\, -2f + 3 \\ \hline 5f - 7 \end{aligned}$$

3.
$$\begin{aligned} r^2 - 3r \\ (+)\, r^2 + 4r - 1 \\ \hline 2r^2 + r - 1 \end{aligned}$$

4.
$$\begin{aligned} 9m^2 - 3n \\ (+)\quad 3n - 5 \\ \hline 9n^2 - 5 \end{aligned}$$

5.
$$\begin{aligned} w^2 - 3w + 3 \\ (+)\, w^2 + 4w + 1 \\ \hline 2w^2 + w + 4 \end{aligned}$$

6.
$$\begin{aligned} 8c^2 - 4c + 6 \\ (+)\, c^2 + c - 1 \\ \hline 9c^2 - 3c + 5 \end{aligned}$$

7.
$$\begin{aligned} -p^2 + 6p + 8 \\ (+)\, p^2 - 4p - 5 \\ \hline 2p + 3 \end{aligned}$$

8.
$$\begin{aligned} 3v^2 + v \\ (+)\, -2w + 7 \\ \hline 3v^2 - v + 7 \end{aligned}$$

9.
$$\begin{aligned} 6m^2 + m + 1 \\ (+)\, 2m^2 - 2m - 3 \\ \hline 8m^2 - m - 2 \end{aligned}$$

10.
$$\begin{aligned} 5d^2 + 7d - 4 \\ (+)\, 5d^2 - 6d - 4 \\ \hline 10d^2 + d - 8 \end{aligned}$$

11. $(2r^2 - 3) + (-r^2 + 4r + 1)$
$r^2 + 4r - 2$

12. $(g^2 + 2g + 5) + (5g^2 - 2g + 3)$
$6g^2 + 8$

13. $(-m - 9) + (3m - 3)$
$2m - 12$

14. $(2x^2 + 8x - 7) + (3x + 5)$
$2x^2 + 11x - 2$

15. $(k^2 - k) + (7k^2 - k - 2)$
$8k^2 - 2k - 2$

16. $(4a^2 + 3ab) + (ab + 2b^2)$
$4a^2 + 4ab + 2b^2$

17. $(5c - 7) + (3c^2 - 4c + 6)$
$3c^2 + c - 1$

18. $(x^2 + xy) + (xy + y^2)$
$x^2 + 2xy + y^2$

19. $(-h^2 + 3h - 6) + (4h^2 - 2h + 3)$
$3h^2 + h - 3$

20. $(x^2 + x + 1) + (2x - 9x^2)$
$-8x^2 + 3x + 1$

21. $(6g^2 - 2g - 3) + (2g^2 + 5g)$
$8g^2 + 3g - 3$

22. $(b^2 + b + 1) + (b^2 - b - 1)$
$2b^2$

23. $(2y^2 - 7y + 9) + (y^2 - 4y - 6)$
$3y^2 - 11y + 3$

24. $(7p^3 - 4) + (2p^2 + 5p + 1)$
$7p^3 + 2p^2 + 5p - 3$

Answers (Lesson 13-2)

Word Problem Practice sheet (Lesson 13-2)

NAME _____ DATE _____ PERIOD _____

13-2 Word Problem Practice
Adding Polynomials

1. TELEPHONE PLAN A phone plan with XYZ Cellular costs $49 per month, with additional fees of t per text message and e per minute for any extra minutes not covered by the plan. Aaron sent 13 text messages and used 7 extra minutes in January, and sent 8 text messages and used 27 extra minutes in February. Write an expression representing Aaron's two month telephone bill.

$98 + 21t + 34e$

2. GARDENING Marty and Jack are planning a vegetable garden together. They decide that they want a design with six square pieces in the middle and a 3-foot border around the outside. Write an expression that represents the area of the garden. $6x^2 + 30x + 36$

3. SNACK SALE Susanna and Winston held a snack sale to raise money for a class trip.

They sold drinks for d dollars each and snacks for s dollars each. Starting with $30 to begin with, they sold items according to the table. Write an expression that represents how much money they had at the end of the snack sale.

Item	Number Sold
Lemonade	20
Fruit Punch	34
Apple	18
Pretzel	9
Granola Bar	28

$30 + 54d + 55s$

4. ANCIENT ART A *mosaic* is a panel made up of objects, such as broken glass or seashells, that form a design. One method for producing mosaic, which the ancient Greeks and Romans often used, was to press tiles into grout. Held in place by the grout, some of the designs have survived for thousands of years. Suppose an artisan wanted to create a square mosaic panel measuring x inches on a side by first lining the edges with a row of tiles that measured 1 inch square. Write an expression to represent the number of square edge tiles needed for the panel. Sample answers: $4x - 4$ or $4(x - 1)$

$x = 6$

PRINT SHOP For Exercises 5 and 6, use the following information.
A small business provides a photocopying and printing service for its customers. Its prices are listed in the table.

Product	Price Each
Greeting Card	$0.50
Folded Brochure	$1.00
Poster	$4.25

5. Write the polynomial expression that represents the total cost of a print job that includes c cards, b brochures, and p posters.

$0.5c + b + 4.25p$

6. If a copy job costs $232.50 in total and includes 100 greeting cards and 55 brochures, how many posters were included?

30 posters

Practice sheet (Lesson 13-2)

NAME _____ DATE _____ PERIOD _____

13-2 Practice
Adding Polynomials

Find each sum.

1.
$8q + 3$
$(+) 4q - 2$
$\overline{12q + 1}$

2.
$9f - 3$
$(+) -f - 15$
$\overline{8f - 18}$

3.
$4j^2 + 11r$
$(+) 5r^2 - 3r - 7$
$\overline{9r^2 + 8r - 7}$

4.
$n^2 - 3n$
$(+)\ 3n - 10$
$\overline{n^2 - 10}$

5.
$6w^2 + 2w + 7$
$(+) 8w^2 + 3w - 9$
$\overline{14w^2 + 5w - 2}$

6.
$8c^2 - 3c + 15$
$(+) 3c^2 + 3c - 11$
$\overline{11c^2 + 4}$

7.
$-5p^2 - 2p + 4$
$(+) 5p^2 + 2p - 4$
$\overline{0}$

8.
$7v^2 - 2v$
$(+) 7v^2 - v + 5$
$\overline{14v^2 - 3v + 5}$

9.
$5m^2 + 6m - 3$
$(+) 8m^2 + 9m - 2$
$\overline{13m^2 + 15m - 5}$

10.
$7d^2 + 8d - 3$
$(+) d^2 + d + 3$
$\overline{8d^2 + 9d}$

11. $(r^2 + 9) + (-4r^2 + 6r + 10)$
$-3r^2 + 6r + 19$

12. $(g^2 + 3g - 6) + (6g^2 - 6g + 1)$
$7g^2 - 3g - 5$

13. $(-2m + 10) + (5m - 3)$
$3m + 7$

14. $(4x^2 - 7x) + (8x + 5)$
$4x^2 + x + 5$

15. $(3k^2 + 9k) + (k^2 - 2k - 4)$
$4k^2 + 7k - 4$

16. $(2a^2 - 3ab) + (4ab - 8b^2)$
$2a^2 + ab - 8b^2$

17. $(c + 4) + (c^2 - c + 6)$
$c^2 + 10$

18. $(5x^2 - 3xy) + (2xy + 9y^2)$
$5x^2 - xy + 9y^2$

19. $(2y^3 + y^2 + 5) + (2y^2 + 3y)$
$2y^3 + 3y^2 + 3y + 5$

20. $(-5p^2 + 6p - 7) + (p^2 - 2)$
$-4p^2 + 6p - 9$

21. $(3ab^2 - 2a - 1) + (a^2 + ab + 3)$
$3ab^2 + a^2 - 2a + ab + 2$

22. $(6rs^3 + 4r) + (5rs^3 + 7)$
$11rs^3 + 4r + 7$

23. **GEOMETRY** The lengths of the sides of a triangle are $(x^2 - 5)$, $(7x - 1)$, and x. Find the perimeter of the triangle. $x^2 + 8x - 6$

13-2 Enrichment

NAME _____ DATE _____ PERIOD _____

Adding Polynomials

Can you make a sentence using these words?

A FRUIT TIME LIKE AN BUT FLIES BANANA ARROW LIKE FLIES

Add the polynomials. Then find the word in the table at the right that corresponds to the sum. Read the words in order down the column to discover the hidden saying.

Word

1. $(2x^2 + 3x^2) + (5x^2 + x^2)$ $11x^2$ TIME

2. $(2x^2 + 3x^3) + (5x^2 + x^2)$ $3x^3 + 8x^2$ FLIES

3. $(2x^2 + x) + (xy + x)$ $2x^2 + 2x + xy$ LIKE

4. $(x^3 + 2x^2) + (5x^3 + x)$ $6x^3 + 2x^2 + x$ AN

5. $(x + xy) + (x^2 + xy)$ $x^2 + 2xy + x$ ARROW

6. $(5x^2 + x) + (x + 2x^4)$ $2x^4 + 5x^2 + 2x$ BUT

7. $(xy + y^2 + x^2) + (2xy + x^2)$ $2x^2 + 3xy + y^2$ FRUIT

8. $(3x^2 + 2x^3) + (x^3 + x)$ $3x^3 + 3x^2 + x$ FLIES

9. $(x + x^2) + x^3$ $x^3 + x^2 + x$ LIKE

10. $(x^3 + x^3) + (x^3 + x^3)$ $4x^3$ A

11. $2x^{12} + 2x^{12}$ $4x^{12}$ BANANA

Word	
$4x^3$	A
$2x^2 + 3xy + y^2$	FRUIT
$11x^2$	TIME
$x^3 + x^2 + x$	LIKE
$6x^3 + 2x^2 + x$	AN
$2x^4 + 5x^2 + 2x$	BUT
$3x^3 + 8x^2$	FLIES
$4x^{12}$	BANANA
$x^2 + 2xy + x$	ARROW
$2x^2 + 2x + xy$	LIKE
$3x^3 + 3x^2 + x$	FLIES

13-3 Lesson Reading Guide

NAME _____ DATE _____ PERIOD _____

Subtracting Polynomials

Get Ready for the Lesson

Read the introduction to Lesson 13-3 in your textbook. Write your answers below.

a. What is the difference in degrees and the difference in minutes between the two stations? **4 degrees, 8.1 minutes**

b. Explain how you can find the difference in latitude between any two locations, given the degrees and minutes. **Subtract the degrees and subtract the minutes.**

c. The longitude of Station 1 is 162°16'36" and the longitude of Station 5 is 68°8'2". Find the difference in longitude between the two stations. **94°8'34"**

Read the Lesson

1. Show how to find the difference $(3x^2 + x + 2) - (2x^2 - 7)$ by aligning like terms and by adding the additive inverse.

Like Terms

$$3x^2 + x + 2$$
$$(-)\ 2x^2\ \ \ \ \ - 7$$
$$\overline{\ x^2 + x + 9}$$

Additive Inverse

$$3x^2 + x + 2$$
$$(+)\ -2x^2\ \ \ \ \ + 7$$
$$\overline{\ x^2 + x + 9}$$

2. Which method do you prefer? Why? **Answers will vary.**

Remember What You Learned

3. a. You have learned to subtract polynomials by adding the additive inverse. Look up *inverse* in the dictionary. What is its definition? How does this help you remember how to find the additive inverse? **Opposite; you change each sign to the opposite and then add instead of subtract.**

b. Write the additive inverses of the polynomials in the table below.

Polynomial	Additive Inverse
$x^2 + 2x - 3$	$-x^2 - 2x + 3$
$6x - 8$	$-6x + 8$
$5x^2 + 8y^2 - 2xy$	$-5x^2 - 8y^2 + 2xy$

Answers (Lesson 13-3)

NAME _____ DATE _____ PERIOD _____

13-3 Skills Practice
Subtracting Polynomials

Find each difference.

1.
$7y + 5$
$(-)\ y + 6$
____
$6y - 1$

2.
$k + 8$
$(-)\ 2k - 9$
____
$-k + 17$

3.
$w^2 + w + 1$
$(-)\ 2w^2 + 3w + 2$
____
$-w^2 - 2w - 1$

4.
$c^2 - 7c + 2$
$(-)\ -c^2 - c - 1$
____
$2c^2 - 6c + 3$

5.
$3d^2 - d$
$(-)\ d^2 - 3d - 8$
____
$2d^2 + 2d + 8$

6.
$7n^2 - 3n$
$(-)\ -n^2 - 3n - 1$
____
$8n^2 + 1$

7.
$2m^2 - 5m + 3$
$(-)\ 5m^2 - m - 3$
____
$-3m^2 - 4m + 6$

8.
$d^2 - 3d - 6$
$(-)\ d^2 - 2d - 1$
____
$-d - 5$

9.
$-q^2 + 2q + 2$
$(-)\ q^2 - 7q + 9$
____
$-2q^2 + 9q - 7$

10.
$v^2 + v$
$(-)\ 8v^2 - 8v + 8$
____
$-7v^2 + 9v - 8$

11. $(r^2 - 10r - 3) - (-r^2 - r + 1)$
$2r^2 - 9r - 4$

12. $(7k^2 + k + 8) - (2k^2 - 3k - 3)$
$5k^2 + 4k + 11$

13. $(a^2 - 9) - (a - 4)$
$a^2 - a - 5$

14. $(4x^2 + 11x - 7) - (x^2 - 3x - 6)$
$3x^2 + 14x - 1$

15. $(k^2 - 3k) - (2k^2 - 7k - 1)$
$-k^2 + 4k + 1$

16. $(5a^2 + ab) - (ab + 3b^2)$
$5a^2 - 3b^2$

17. $(5u^2 - 7) - (3u^2 - 4u + 6)$
$2u^2 + 4u - 13$

18. $(4m^2 + mn) - (3mn + n^2)$
$4m^2 - 2mn - n^2$

19. $(h^2 + 3h = 6) - (h^2 - 2h - 3)$
$5h - 3$

20. $(x^2 - x - 1) - (2x + 9x^2)$
$-8x^2 - 3x - 1$

21. $(6g^2 + 3g + 3) - (g^2 + g - 5)$
$5g^2 + 2g + 8$

22. $(b^2 + b + 1) - (b^2 - b - 1)$
$2b + 2$

23. $(a^2 - 9a - 10) - (a^2 - a - 4)$
$-8a - 6$

24. $(4r^2 + 7r) - (3r^2 - 2r + 7)$
$r^2 + 9r - 7$

Chapter 13   19   *Glencoe Pre-Algebra*

NAME _____ DATE _____ PERIOD _____

13-3 Study Guide and Intervention
Subtracting Polynomials

Subtract Polynomials To subtract polynomials, subtract like terms.

Example Find $(x^2 + 3x - 6) - (4x^2 - 1)$.

Method 1 Subtract vertically.
$x^2 + 3x - 6$
$(-)\ 4x^2\qquad - 1$
____
$-3x^2 + 3x - 5$

Method 2 Add the additive inverse of $4x^2 - 1$, which is $(-1)(4x^2 - 1)$ or $-4x^2 + 1$.
$= (x^2 + 3x - 6) - (4x^2 - 1)$
$= (x^2 + 3x - 6) + (-4x^2 + 1)$
$= (x^2 - 4x^2) + (3x) + (-6 + 1)$
$= -3x^2 + 3x - 5$

Exercises
Find each difference.

1.
$4c + 7$
$(-)\ 3c + 3$
____
$c + 4$

2.
$2m + 5$
$(-)\ -8m + 1$
____
$10m + 4$

3.
$9k^2 - 4k + 5$
$(-)\ k^2\qquad - 5$
____
$8k^2 - 4k + 10$

4.
$3z^2 - z$
$(-)\qquad 3z - 5$
____
$3z^2 - 4z + 5$

5. $(-6r + 3) - (7r + 2)$
$-13r + 1$

6. $(8f^2 - 7f - 3) - (2f + 4)$
$8f^2 - 9f - 7$

7. $(5n^2 - 2n) - (3n + 9)$
$5n^2 - 5n - 9$

8. $(a^2 + 5ab) - (-2ab - 3b^2)$
$a^2 + 7ab + 3b^2$

9. $(6g^2 + 8) - (5g^2 - 2g + 6)$
$g^2 + 2g + 2$

10. $(8x^2 - 3y) - (2xy + 3y)$
$8x^2 - 2xy - 6y$

11. $(n - 12) - (n^2 + n + 9)$
$-n^2 - 21$

12. $(h^2 - 2h + 1) - (3h - 7h^2)$
$8h^2 - 5h + 1$

13. $(y^2 + y + 1) - (y^2 - y + 1)$
$2y$

14. $(6p^2 - 5p - 1) - (2p - 4)$
$6p^2 - 7p + 3$

15. $(4q^2 + q) - (q^2 + 3)$
$3q^2 + q - 3$

16. $(6v^2 + 8) - (7v^2 + 2v - 5)$
$-v^2 - 2v + 13$

17. $(u^2 + u - 4) - (5u^2 - 4)$
$-4u^2 + u$

18. $(9b^2 + 2) - (-b^2 + b + 9)$
$10b^2 - b - 7$

Chapter 13   18   *Glencoe Pre-Algebra*

Answers (Lesson 13-3)

NAME _____ DATE _____ PERIOD _____

13-3 Word Problem Practice
Subtracting Polynomials

1. **GEOGRAPHY** The highest point in the state of Oklahoma is Black Mesa and the lowest point is the Little River. The difference in elevation between these two points is 176 meters more than the sum of the elevations. What is the elevation of the lowest point in Oklahoma?
88 meters

2. **TAXI FARES** The rate for a taxicab in Austin is \$3.50 for the first mile plus \$2 for each additional mile. In Houston, the taxi rate is \$4 for the first mile and \$1.80 for every mile thereafter. What is the difference between the taxi rates of these two cities? **\$0.50 − \$0.20x**

3. **GEOMETRY** The perimeter of the isosceles triangle is $8x − 3$ inches. Find the length of the third side.

(triangle labeled $3x − 2$)

$(2x + 1)$ in.

4. **POSTERS** Pam and her friends are making a poster for the clothing drive at school. They decide on the design below. Each rectangle will be outlined with ribbon. Write an expression to show how much more ribbon Pam and her friends will need for the larger rectangle than for the smaller one.

(diagram: $4x + 5$, $2x + 3$, $2x$, $x − 4$)

$6x + 12$ units

INTERIOR DECORATING For Exercises 5 and 6, use the following information. Shayla is putting up a wallpaper border on the walls in her room. The border comes in pieces that are x feet long. Shayla figures that she will need 4 pieces plus an extra 3 feet of border to trim the long wall of her room.

5. Write the polynomial expression that represents the length of her room.
$4x + 3$ ft

6. The total amount of border Shayla used was $14x + 10$ feet. Write the polynomial expression that represents the width of her room.
$3x + 2$ ft

Chapter 13   21   *Glencoe Pre-Algebra*

NAME _____ DATE _____ PERIOD _____

13-3 Practice
Subtracting Polynomials

Find each difference.

1.
$$4y + 1$$
$$(-)\ 3y + 8$$
$$y − 7$$

2.
$$2k + 3$$
$$(-)\ 7k − 6$$
$$-5k + 9$$

3.
$$5j^2 + 2j − 2$$
$$(-)\ j^2 + 9j + 2$$
$$4j^2 − 7j − 4$$

4.
$$c^2 + 5c − 3$$
$$(-)\ -c^2 − 5c − 1$$
$$2c^2 + 10c − 2$$

5.
$$d^2 − 4d + 6$$
$$(-)\ d^2 + 3d − 8$$
$$-7d + 14$$

6.
$$2n^2 − 3n − 10$$
$$(-)\ -n^2 − 3n + 8$$
$$3n^2 − 18$$

7.
$$9m^2 − 4m + 13$$
$$(-)\ 7m^2 − 2m − 3$$
$$2m^2 − 2m + 16$$

8.
$$d^2 + 3d − 6$$
$$(-)\ d^2 + 3d + 6$$
$$-12$$

9.
$$-6q^2 − 3q + 2$$
$$(-)\ 3q^2 + 4q + 4$$
$$-9q^2 − 7q − 2$$

10.
$$u^2 − v$$
$$(-)\ 2u^2 − 9v − 3$$
$$-v^2 + 8v + 3$$

11. $(4n^2 − n − 6) − (−2n^2 − 3n − 14)$
$$6n^2 + 2n + 8$$

12. $(3k^2 + 9k) − (8k^2 − 12)$
$$-5k^2 + 9k + 12$$

13. $(k^2 − 7) − (k − 11)$
$$k^2 − k + 4$$

14. $(9x^2 − x − 2) − (3x^2 − x − 4)$
$$6x^2 + 2$$

15. $(k^2 − 12) − (k^2 + 6k − 9)$
$$-6k − 3$$

16. $(k^2 + 4kb) − (5kb + 2b^2)$
$$k^2 − kb − 2b^2$$

17. $(3u^2 − 9) − (u^2 + 21u + 2)$
$$2u^2 − 21u − 11$$

18. $(5m^2 − 4mn) − (4mn + 8n^2)$
$$5m^2 − 8mn − 8n^2$$

19. $(h^2 + 8h + 5) − (h^2 − 3h − 7)$
$$11h + 12$$

20. $(2x^2 − 4x − 8) − (2x − 8x^2)$
$$10x^2 − 6x − 8$$

21. $(6g^2 + 3g + 2) − (g^2 + g − 4)$
$$5g^2 + 2g + 6$$

22. $(b^3 + b^2 − ab) − (b^3 + 3b^2 + 5)$
$$-2b^2 − ab − 5$$

23. **POOLS** A swimming pool is $(4w^2 − 16)$ feet long and $(w − 16)$ feet wide. How much longer is the length than the width? **$4w^2 − w$ ft**

Chapter 13   20   *Glencoe Pre-Algebra*

NAME _____ DATE _____ PERIOD _____

13-4 Lesson Reading Guide

Multiplying a Polynomial by a Monomial

Get Ready for the Lesson

Read the introduction to Lesson 13-4 in your textbook. **Write your answers below.**

a. Write an expression that represents the area of the rectangular region outlined on the photo. $w(2w - 52)$

b. Recall that $2(4 + 1) = 2(4) + 2(1)$ by the Distributive Property. Use this property to simplify the expression you wrote in part a. $2w^2 - 52w$

c. The Grande Arche is approximately w feet deep. Explain how you can write a polynomial to represent the volume of the hollowed-out region of the building. Then write the polynomial. **Use the Distributive Property to multiply $2w^2 - 52w$ by w; $2w^3 - 52w^2$**

Read the Lesson

1. Draw a model that shows the product $x(x + 2)$. Write the polynomial that shows the product. **See students' work. $x^2 + 2x$**

2. Explain the Distributive Property and give an example of how it is used to multiply a polynomial by a monomial. **Sample answer: Multiply each number inside the parentheses by the number outside the parentheses.**
$$2(3y + 2) = 2(3y) + 2(2)$$
$$= 6y + 4$$

Remember What You Learned

3. *Distribute* is a common word in the English language.

a. Find the definition of *distribute* in a dictionary. Write the definition that most closely relates to this lesson. **to deliver to members of a group**

b. Explain how this definition can help you remember how to use the Distributive Property to multiply a polynomial by a monomial. **The number outside the parentheses is "distributed" to each number inside.**

Chapter 13   23   *Glencoe Pre-Algebra*

NAME _____ DATE _____ PERIOD _____

13-3 Enrichment

Polynomials with Fractional Coefficients

Polynomials may have fractional coefficients in some or all of the terms. Computation with these types of polynomials is done in the same way as with whole-number coefficients.

Add or subtract. Write all coefficients as fractions.

1. Add $\frac{3}{4}x^2 + \frac{2}{5}y^2$ and $\frac{1}{6}x^2 - \frac{4}{3}y^2$. $\frac{11}{12}x^2 - \frac{14}{15}y^2$

2. From $\frac{1}{2}x^2 - \frac{1}{3}xy^2 + \frac{1}{4}y^2$, take $\frac{1}{3}x^2 - \frac{5}{2}xy + \frac{5}{6}y^2$. $\frac{1}{6}x^2 - \frac{1}{3}xy^2 + \frac{1}{2}xy - \frac{7}{12}y^2$

3. Add $\frac{3}{2}x - \frac{4}{3}y$, $\frac{7}{8}x - \frac{6}{7}y$, and $y - \frac{1}{4}x$. $\frac{3}{8}x - \frac{25}{21}y$

4. Subtract $\frac{1}{6}x^2 + \frac{1}{8}x - \frac{1}{4}$ from $\frac{2}{3}x^2 + \frac{5}{8}x + \frac{1}{2}$. $\frac{1}{2}x^2 + \frac{1}{2}x + \frac{3}{4}$

5. Add $\frac{1}{3}xy + \frac{11}{12}y^2$ to $\frac{4}{9}xy - \frac{1}{6}y^2$. $\frac{7}{9}xy + \frac{3}{4}y^2$

6. Add $\frac{1}{5}x^2 - \frac{1}{8}x - \frac{1}{3}$ and $\frac{3}{10}x^2 + \frac{5}{8}x + \frac{1}{9}$. $\frac{1}{2}x^2 + \frac{1}{2}x - \frac{2}{9}$

7. From $\frac{1}{2} + \frac{2}{3}y + \frac{3}{4}y^2$, take $\frac{1}{8} + \frac{1}{6}y - \frac{5}{2}y^2$. $\frac{3}{8} + \frac{1}{2}y + \frac{19}{12}y^2$

8. Subtract $\frac{7}{12}x - \frac{1}{4}$ from $\frac{3}{4}x - \frac{1}{3}$. $\frac{1}{6}x - \frac{1}{12}$

9. Add $\frac{3}{8}x^2 - \frac{1}{3}xy + \frac{5}{9}y^2$ and $\frac{1}{2}x^2 - \frac{1}{2}xy - \frac{1}{3}y^2$. $\frac{7}{8}x^2 - \frac{5}{6}xy + \frac{2}{9}y^2$

10. Subtract $\frac{3}{4}y^2 + \frac{1}{2}y$ from $\frac{4}{3}y^2 + \frac{7}{8}y$. $\frac{7}{12}y^2 + \frac{3}{8}y$

Chapter 13   22   *Glencoe Pre-Algebra*

NAME _____ DATE _____ PERIOD _____

13-4 Skills Practice

Multiplying a Polynomial by a Monomial

Find each product.

1. $4(k + 7)$
   $4k + 28$
2. $(5h + 3)3$
   $15h + 9$
3. $-9(2q + 7)$
   $-18q - 63$
4. $(6v - 1)(-6)$
   $-36v + 6$
5. $-8(5h - 6)$
   $-40h + 48$
6. $3(12y - 6)$
   $36y - 18$
7. $(9d + 3)4$
   $36d + 12$
8. $-5(5n - 9)$
   $-25n + 45$
9. $2(c^2 + 4)$
   $2x^2 + 8$
10. $-6(5x^2 - 3x)$
    $-30x^2 + 18x$
11. $(4x^2 - 6x - 9)9$
    $36x^2 - 54x - 81$
12. $-7(2c^2 - 8c + 5)$
    $-14c^2 + 56c - 35$
13. $g(2g + 5)$
    $2g^2 + 5g$
14. $-b(9b - 6)$
    $-9b^2 + 6b$
15. $(4y + 7)7y$
    $4y^2 + 7y$
16. $(2j - 1)(-j)$
    $-2j^2 + j$
17. $-c(c - 2)$
    $-c^2 + 2c$
18. $h(6h + 4)$
    $6h^2 + 4h$
19. $(6k + 6)(-k)$
    $-6k^2 - 6k$
20. $p(3p - 8)$
    $3p^2 - 8p$
21. $-a(8a + 2)$
    $-8a^2 - 2a$
22. $r(r^2 + 7r)$
    $r^3 + 7r^2$
23. $x(4x^2 - 2x - 1)$
    $4x^3 - 2x^2 - x$
24. $ab(3ab + 2a)$
    $3a^2b^2 + 2a^2b$
25. $x(4xy - 3y^2)$
    $4x^2y - 3xy^2$
26. $(gh - h)(-g)$
    $-g^2h + gh$
27. $x(4x^2 - xy + y^2)$
    $4x^3 - x^2y + xy^2$
28. $6v(3v + 9)$
    $18v^2 + 54v$
29. $(u + 4)(-5u)$
    $-5u^2 - 20u$
30. $8b(b - 6)$
    $8b^2 - 48b$
31. $-7d(5d - 9)$
    $-35d^2 + 63d$
32. $(8w - 4)w$
    $8w^2 - 4w$
33. $a(7a + 4)$
    $7a^2 + 4a$
34. $(6y - 6)(-y^2)$
    $-6y^3 + 6y^2$
35. $s(s + 1)$
    $s^2 + s$
36. $-m(6m - 7)$
    $-6m^2 + 7m$
37. $-k^2(2k - 3)$
    $-2k^3 + 3k^2$
38. $c(7c^2 + 3c - 4)$
    $7c^3 + 3c^2 - 4c$
39. $7mn(m + 2mn + 4n)$
    $7m^2n + 14m^2n^2 + 28mn^2$
40. $8a(a + ab + b)$
    $8a^2 + 8a^2b + 8ab$
41. $(xy - y^2)(-4xy)$
    $-4x^2y^2 + 4xy^3$
42. $-8u(7u^2 - 2uv + 4v^2)$
    $-56u^3 + 16u^2v - 32uv^2$

NAME _____ DATE _____ PERIOD _____

13-4 Study Guide and Intervention

Multiplying a Polynomial by a Monomial

The Distributive Property can be used to multiply a polynomial by a monomial.

Example 1 Find $7(4x - 8)$.

$7(4x - 8) = 7(4x) - 7(8)$
$= 28x - 56$

Example 2 Find $(x^2 - 5x + 4)(-2x)$.

$(x^2 - 5x + 4)(-2x) = x^2(-2x) - 5x(-2x) + 4(-2x)$
$= -2x^3 + 10x^2 - 8x$

Exercises

Find each product.

1. $5(7y + 4)$
   $35y + 20$
2. $(3h + 6)4$
   $12h + 24$
3. $-9(q + 8)$
   $-9q - 72$
4. $6(d - 2)$
   $6d - 12$
5. $(4g - 5)(-2)$
   $-8g + 10$
6. $-7(4x^2 - 7)$
   $-28x^2 + 49$
7. $-2(n^2 - 3n + 9)$
   $-2n^2 + 6n - 18$
8. $(a^2 - 2ab + b^2)5$
   $5a^2 - 10ab + 5b^2$
9. $r(r + 9)$
   $r^2 + 9r$
10. $(b^2 - 4)(-b)$
    $-b^3 + 4b$
11. $-x(3x + 6)$
    $-3x^2 - 6x$
12. $(2k - 9)(k^2)$
    $2k^3 - 9k^2$
13. $-m(6m + 1)$
    $-6m^2 - m$
14. $p(7p - 2)$
    $7p^2 - 2p$
15. $(8 - 3h)(-h)$
    $3h^2 - 8h$
16. $w(4w^2 - 2w + 3)$
    $4w^3 - 2w^2 + 3w$
17. $ab(2a + b)$
    $2a^2b + ab^2$
18. $x(7x + y)$
    $7x^2 + xy$
19. $(m^2 - mn - n)m$
    $m^3 - m^2n - mn$
20. $2y(5y + 1)$
    $10y^2 + 2y$
21. $-10u(u - 5)$
    $-10u^2 + 50u$
22. $(5r^2 - 2r)(-3r)$
    $-15r^3 + 6r^2$
23. $8z(2z + 7)$
    $16z^2 + 56z$
24. $5b^2(6b - 2)$
    $30b^3 - 10b^2$
25. $4p(6p^2 + 3p)$
    $24p^4 + 12p^3$
26. $(5u^2 - 2v - 4)(-2v)$
    $-10v^3 + 4v^2 + 8v$
27. $8y^3(3y^2 - y + 8)$
    $24y^5 - 8y^4 + 64y^3$
28. $3m(2m + 4n)$
    $6m^2 + 12mn$
29. $(8gh - 3h)(-3gh)$
    $-24g^2h^2 + 9gh^2$
30. $5a(2a - 3ab + b)$
    $10a^2 - 15a^2b + 5ab$

Answers (Lesson 13-4)

Page 26 (Practice)

NAME _____ DATE _____ PERIOD _____

13-4 Practice

Multiplying a Polynomial by a Monomial

Find each product.

1. $5(3k + 8)$
$15k + 40$

2. $(3h + 6)2$
$6h + 12$

3. $-2(q - 4)$
$-2q + 8$

4. $(3v - 5)(-7)$
$-21v + 35$

5. $11(4d - 7)$
$44d - 77$

6. $-8(12c - 6)$
$-96c + 48$

7. $(5g - 10)(-5)$
$-25g + 50$

8. $2(5p - 10)$
$10p - 20$

9. $-9(3f^2 - 2f - 1)$
$-27f^2 + 18f + 9$

10. $2.5(8w + 5)$
$20w + 12.5$

11. $(4r^3 - 3r)(-8)$
$-32r^3 + 24r$

12. $-6(3x^2 - 2x + 7)$
$-18x^2 + 12x - 42$

13. $n(7n + 3)$
$7n^2 + 3n$

14. $(6u - 15)(-u)$
$-6u^2 + 15u$

15. $-h(8h + 2)$
$-8h^2 - 2h$

16. $(8y + 3)(-y)$
$-8y^2 - 3y$

17. $a(4a - 4)$
$4a^2 - 4a$

18. $(5p + 15)(-p)$
$-5p^2 - 15p$

19. $-d(-5d + 1)$
$5d^2 - d$

20. $-g(1.8g + 10)$
$-1.8g^2 - 10g$

21. $m(0.9m^2 - 0.5)$
$0.9m^3 - 0.5m$

22. $(2q^3 - 5q^2 - 2q)(-q)$
$-2q^4 + 5q^3 + 2q^2$

23. $k^3(7k^4 - 2k^2 + 6)$
$7k^7 - 2k^5 + 6k^3$

24. $ab(10a^2b + 3a)$
$10a^3b^2 + 3a^2b$

25. $y^2(5x - 2xy + y)$
$5xy^2 - 2xy^3 + y^3$

26. $n(8 - m - 12mn^2)$
$8n - mn - 12mn^3$

27. $(4gh^2 - 2g^2 - h)(-g^2)$
$-4g^3h^2 + 2g^4 + g^2h$

28. $(20q - 4)(-2q)$
$-40q^2 + 8q$

29. $14k(2k + 5)$
$28k^2 + 70k$

30. $(9p - 7)(-3p^2)$
$-27p^3 + 21p^2$

31. $(0.2c - 1)(-1.5c^2)$
$-0.3c^3 + 1.5c^2$

32. $-6.5n(4n^2 - 8)$
$-26n^3 + 52n$

33. $-6x^2(4x^2 - 10x)$
$-24x^4 + 60x^3$

34. $5h^2(2h^3 - h^2 - 7h + 8)$
$10h^5 - 5h^4 - 35h^3 + 40h^2$

35. $(4y^2 - 3y + 9)(-2y)$
$-8y^3 + 6y^2 - 18y$

36. $6gh(8g^2 + 4gh + 3h^2)$
$48g^3h + 24g^2h^2 + 18gh^3$

37. $10a(2a^2 - 5ab + 4a)$
$20a^3 - 50a^2b + 40a^2$

38. $(8x^2 - 3xy - xy^2)(-7x)$
$-56x^3 + 21x^2y + 7x^2y^2$

39. $-5c^2(2cd - d^2 + 1)$
$-10c^3d + 5c^2d^2 - 5c^2$

40. Find the area of a porch that is 3x feet wide and 4x + 9 feet long.
$12x^2 + 27x$ ft^2

Chapter 13   26   *Glencoe Pre-Algebra*

Page 27 (Word Problem Practice)

NAME _____ DATE _____ PERIOD _____

13-4 Word Problem Practice

Multiplying a Polynomial by a Monomial

1. **BOOKS** The largest published book in the world is Michael Hawley's *Bhutan: A Visual Odyssey Across the Kingdom*. The length of a page is 3 feet shorter than twice its width. The perimeter of a page is 24 feet. What are the dimensions of the book?
5 ft by 7 ft

2. **GEOMETRY** Find the area of the shaded region. Write in simplest form.

$6x^2 + 10x$ square units

3. **FOOTBALL** The dimensions of Canadian football fields are different than the dimensions of American football fields. Use the information in the table to find the length and width of each football field.

Playing Field Plus End Zones		
Measure	American (ft)	Canadian (ft)
Perimeter	1040	1290
Width	w	w
Length	2w + 40	(2w + 40) + 20

American: 360 ft by 160 ft;
Canadian: 450 ft by 195 ft

4. **FLAGS** The largest flag flown from a flagstaff is a Brazilian national flag in Brasilia, Brazil. The width of the flag is 20 meters more than half the length. Find the area of the flag. Write in simplest form
$\frac{1}{2}\ell^2 + 20\ell$

MANUFACTURING For Exercises 5–7, use the following information.

Casey's Cardboard Company makes different sizes of cardboard boxes. The figure below shows a template for one size cardboard box before it has been cut and folded.

5. Write a simplified expression to represent the surface area of the cardboard box.
$47x^2 - 14x$ in^2

6. Find the surface area of the box if x is 4 inches.
696 in^2

7. Suppose a side is extended to so the box will be completely enclosed when it is put together. Write a simplified expression to represent the surface area of the enclosed box.
$62x^2 - 20x$ in^2

Chapter 13   27   *Glencoe Pre-Algebra*

Left Page

13-4 Enrichment

Polynomials and Volume

The volume of a rectangular prism can be written as the product of three polynomials. Recall that the volume equals the length times the width times the height.

The two prisms at the right represent the cube of y and the cube of x.

Multiply to find the volume of each prism. Write each answer as an algebraic expression.

1. x^2y

2. xy^2

3. $xy(x - y)$ or $x^2y - xy^2$

4. $xy(x + y)$ or $x^2y + xy^2$

5. $y^2(x - y)$ or $xy^2 - y^3$

6. $y^2(x + y)$ or $xy^2 + y^3$

Multiply, then add to find each volume. Write each answer as an algebraic expression.

7. $2y^3 + y^2(x - y) + xy(x - y)$ or $y^3 + x^2y$

8. $x^2(x - y) + x^2y$ or $x^3 + y^3$

9. $y^3 + x^2y + y^2(x - y) + xy(x + y)$ or $2x^2y + 2xy^2$

Right Page

13-4 Graphing Calculator Activity

Polynomials

A graphing calculator can be used to verify solutions to polynomial arithmetic.

Example 1 Find each sum or difference.

a. $(8x - 6) + (-9x + 11)$

First, find the sum.

$(8x - 6) + (-9x + 11) = -x + 5$

To verify the solution, enter the original expression, $(8x - 6) + (-9x + 11)$, into **Y1** and the sum, $-x + 5$, into **Y2**. Compare the graphs of both.

Keystrokes: Y= (8 X,T,θ,n − 6) + ((−) 9 X,T,θ,n +
11) ENTER (−) X,T,θ,n + 5 ZOOM 6.

The graphs coincide, so the expressions are equivalent. Thus, the solution is correct.

[-10, 10] scl:1 by [-10, 10] scl:1

b. $4a^2 + 7a + 4 - (3a^2 + 2)$

Find the difference.

$4a^2 + 7a + 4 - (3a^2 + 2) = a^2 + 7a + 2$

Enter the original expression into **Y1** and the difference in **Y2**. Compare the graphs.

Keystrokes: Y= X,T,θ,n x^2 + 7 X,T,θ,n + 4 − (3
X,T,θ,n x^2 + 2) ENTER X,T,θ,n x^2 + 7 X,T,θ,n + 2 GRAPH .

The graphs coincide, so the expressions are equivalent. Thus, the solution is correct.

[-10, 10] scl:1 by [-10, 10] scl:1

Example 2 Find $5a(2a + 3)$.

Find the product.

$5a(2a + 3) = 10a^2 + 15a$

Enter the original expression into **Y1** and the solution into **Y2**. Compare the graphs.

Keystrokes: Y= 5 X,T,θ,n x^2 (2 X,T,θ,n + 3) ENTER 10 X,T,θ,n
x^2 + 15 X,T,θ,n GRAPH .

The graphs coincide, so the expressions are equivalent. Thus, the solution is correct.

[-10, 10] scl:1 by [-10, 10] scl:1

Exercises

Perform the stated operation.

1. $(x^2 + 4x + 12) + (-5x^2 + 8)$
   $-4x^2 + 4x + 20$

2. $(16x^2 + 3x + 9) - (2x^2 + 8x + 1)$
   $14x^2 - 5x + 8$

3. $7(-2x^2 + 5x - 11)$
   $-14x^2 + 35x - 77$

4. $6x(-2x^2 + 8x + 2)$
   $-12x^3 + 48x^2 + 12x$

Answers (Lesson 13-5)

13-5 Study Guide and Intervention

Linear and Nonlinear Functions

Linear functions have constant rates of change. Their graphs are straight lines and their equations can be written in the form $y = mx + b$. Nonlinear functions do not have constant rates of change and their graphs are not straight lines.

Example 1   Determine whether each equation represents a *linear* or *nonlinear* function.

a. $y = 9$

This is linear because it can be written as $y = 0x + 9$.

b. $y = x^2 + 4$

This is nonlinear because the exponent of x is not 1, so the equation cannot be written in the form $y = mx + b$.

Tables can represent functions. A nonlinear function does not increase or decrease at a constant rate.

Example 2   Determine whether each table represents a *linear* or *nonlinear* function.

a.

x	y
0	−7
2	1
4	9
6	17

+2 → +8 (each step)

As x increases by 2, y increases by 8. The rate of change is constant, so this is a linear function.

b.

x	y
0	100
5	75
10	0
15	−125

+5 → −25, −75, −125

As x increases by 5, y decreases by a greater amount each time. The rate of change is not constant, so this is a nonlinear function.

Exercises

Determine whether each equation or table represents a *linear* or *nonlinear* function. Explain.

1. $x + 3y = 9$ Linear; equation can be written as $y = -\dfrac{1}{3}x + 3$.

2. $y = \dfrac{8}{x}$ Nonlinear; equation cannot be written in the form $y = mx + b$.

3. $y = 6x(x + 1)$ Nonlinear; equation cannot be written in the form $y = mx + b$.

4. $y = 9 - 5x$ Linear; equation can be written as $y = -5x + 9$.

5.

x	y
0	24
2	14
4	4
6	−6

Linear; rate of change is constant.

6.

x	y
1	1
2	8
3	27
4	64

Nonlinear; rate of change is not constant.

13-5 Lesson Reading Guide

Linear and Nonlinear Functions

Get Ready for the Lesson

Read the introduction to Lesson 13-5 in your textbook. Write your answers below.

a. Write an expression to represent the area of the deck.
$x(40 - 2x)$ or $40x - 2x^2$

b. Find the area of the deck for widths of 6, 8, 10, 12, and 14 feet.
168 ft², 192 ft², 200 ft², 192 ft², 168 ft²

c. Graph the points whose ordered pairs are (width, area). Do the points fall along a straight line? Explain.
No; the connected points fall along a curve.

Read the Lesson 1–3. See students' work.

Write a definition and give an example of each new vocabulary phrase.

Vocabulary	Definition	Example
1. nonlinear function		
2. quadratic function		
3. cubic function		

Remember What You Learned

4. You have learned about linear and nonlinear functions. Nonlinear functions include quadratic functions and cubic functions. Below, write three equations that represent each type of function given. For the nonlinear functions, include at least one quadratic function and one cubic function. Sample answers are given.

Linear	Nonlinear
1. $y = x + 2$	1. $y = x^2 + 1$
2. $y = 2x + 1$	2. $y = 5x^3$
3. $y = \dfrac{x}{-5} - 5$	3. $y = x^2 + 2x - 1$

Answers (Lesson 13-5)

Lesson 13-5

13-5 Practice

Linear and Nonlinear Functions

Determine whether each graph, equation, or table represents a *linear* or *nonlinear* function. Explain.

1. Nonlinear; the graph is a curve.

2. Linear; the graph is a straight line.

3. Linear; the graph is a straight line.

4. $5x - y = 15$ Linear; equation can be written as $y = 5x - 15$.

5. $3y + 12x^2 = 0$ Nonlinear; equation cannot be written in the form $y = mx + b$.

6. $5y - x + 3 = 0$ Linear; equation can be written as $y = \frac{1}{5}x - \frac{3}{5}$.

7. $y = 6\sqrt{x} + 10$ Nonlinear; equation cannot be written in the form $y = mx + b$.

8. $y = \frac{8}{x}$ Nonlinear; equation cannot be written in the form $y = mx + b$.

9. $y = -x^2 + 2$ Nonlinear; equation cannot be written in the form $y = mx + b$.

10.

x	y
1	1.0
2	0.8
3	0.6
4	0.4

Linear; rate of change is constant.

11.

x	y
44	0
48	2.5
52	5.0
56	7.5

Linear; rate of change is constant.

12.

x	y
3	1
6	-2
9	-5
12	-14

Nonlinear; rate of change is not constant.

13. **GEOMETRY** The graph shows how the area of a square increases as the perimeter increases. Is this relationship linear or nonlinear? Explain.

Nonlinear; the graph is not a straight line.

Chapter 13   33   Glencoe Pre-Algebra

13-5 Skills Practice

Linear and Nonlinear Functions

Determine whether each graph, equation, or table represents a *linear* or *nonlinear* function. Explain.

1. Nonlinear; the graph is a curve.

2. Linear; the graph is a straight line.

3. Nonlinear; the graph is a curve.

4. $y = \frac{x}{2} + 1$ Linear; equation can be written as $y = \frac{1}{2}x + 1$.

5. $y = \frac{2}{x} + 10$ Nonlinear; equation cannot be written in the form $y = mx + b$.

6. $y = 8x$ Linear; equation can be written as $y = 8x + 0$.

7. $y = 6$ Linear; equation can be written as $y = 0x + 6$.

8. $2x - y = 5$ Linear; equation can be written as $y = 2x - 5$.

9. $y = x^2 + 4$ Nonlinear; equation cannot be written in the form $y = mx + b$.

10. $y + 4x^2 - 1 = 0$ Nonlinear; equation cannot be written in the form $y = mx + b$.

11. $2y - 8x + 11 = 0$ Linear; equation can be written as $y = 4x - \frac{11}{2}$.

12. $y = \sqrt{3x} - 2$ Nonlinear; equation cannot be written in the form $y = mx + b$.

13.

x	y
1	8
2	5
3	2
4	-1

Linear; rate of change is constant.

14.

x	y
6	1
12	3
18	6
24	10

Nonlinear; rate of change is not constant.

15.

x	y
20	-4
15	-2
10	0
5	2

Linear; rate of change is constant.

Chapter 13   32   Glencoe Pre-Algebra

Chapter 13   A15   Glencoe Pre-Algebra

Answers (Lesson 13-5)

13-5 Word Problem Practice

Linear and Nonlinear Functions

1. TEMPERATURE In the United States, temperature is most often measured in degrees Fahrenheit. Temperature is measured in degrees Celsius in the metric system. The formula used to convert between these two units of measure is $F = \frac{9}{5}C + 32$ where F represents degrees Fahrenheit and C represents degrees Celsius. Does this equation represent a *linear* or *nonlinear* function? **linear**

2. COMPUTER GAMES Suppose the function $-0.005d^2 + 0.12d = h$ is used to simulate the path of a golf ball that is hit off a tee in a computer game. Does this equation represent a *linear* or *nonlinear* function? **nonlinear**

3. GASOLINE The table below shows gasoline prices in Springfield during a one-month period. Is the change in gas price a linear function? Explain. **Nonlinear; the amount of change in price each day is not constant.**

Day of the Month	Price per Gallon
1	$2.57
4	$2.72
7	$2.72
10	$2.88
13	$2.88
16	$2.84
19	$2.76
21	$2.72
24	$2.64
27	$2.60
30	$2.52

4. FOOTBALL PUNTS The function $h = -16t^2 + 90t + 1.5$ represents the height h of the football, in feet, after t seconds when a punter kicks the ball with an upward velocity of 90 feet per second and his foot meets the ball 1.5 feet off the ground. Is this a linear function of time? Explain. **Nonlinear. The height of the football will vary, so the change is not constant.**

FLIGHT RESEARCH For Exercises 5 and 6, use the following information.

The equation $h = -16t^2 + 608t + 4482$ represents the height, h, in feet, of a pilot over time, t, in seconds, after he or she has ejected from a jet and falls to Earth with the aid of a parachute. A pilot is flying at an altitude of approximately 10,000 feet and is forced to eject from the jet. The equation $h = 10,000$ represents an altitude of 10,000 feet.

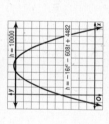

5. Which equation is a linear function? $h = 10,000$

6. Explain why the other equation is a nonlinear function. **Sample answer: The other equation is of the form $y = ax^2 + bx + c$, which is a quadratic equation.**

13-5 Enrichment

David R. Hedgley

African-American mathematician David R. Hedgley, Jr. (1937–) solved one of the most difficult problems in the field of computer graphics—how to program a computer to show any three-dimensional object from a given viewpoint just as the eye would see it. Hedgley's solution helped researchers in aircraft experimentation. Hedgley received an M.S. in Mathematics from California State University in 1970 and a Ph.D. in Computer Science from Somerset University in England in 1988. Hedgley has received numerous national achievement awards.

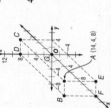

Polynomials in three variables are needed to describe some three-dimensional objects. Each variable represents one of the three dimensions: height, width, and depth.

$P_1: x^2 + y^2 + z^2 + 10x + 4y + 2z - 19$

$P_2: 2x^2 + 2y^2 + 2z^2 - 2x - 3y + 5z - 2$

1. Add the polynomials P_1 and P_2.

$3x^2 + 3y^2 + 3z^2 + 8x + y + 7z - 21$

2. Subtract the polynomials, P_1 from P_2.

$x^2 + y^2 + z^2 - 12x - 7y + 3z + 17$

If the polynomials above were each set equal to zero, they would form equations describing two different spheres in three-dimensional space, or *3-space*. The coordinate plane you studied in Chapter 2 represents *two-space*. You described most lines in that plane by an equation in two variables. Each point on a line could be written as an ordered pair of numbers (x, y). Each point on any figure in 3-space can be written as an *ordered triple* of numbers (x, y, z).

3. What are the values of x, y, and z for point A in the diagram?

$x = 14, y = 4, z = 8$

4. Give the ordered triple representing each of the points B through G in the diagram.

$B(14, 0, 8), C(0, 4, 8), D(0, 0, 8),$
$E(14, 4, 0), F(14, 0, 0), G(0, 0, 0)$

Page (Study Guide and Intervention)

NAME _____ DATE _____ PERIOD _____

13-6 Study Guide and Intervention

Graphing Quadratic and Cubic Functions

To graph a quadratic or cubic function, make a table of values and then plot the points.

Example Graph $y = 2x^3 - 1$.

x	y
−1	−3
0	−1
1	1
1.2	2.5

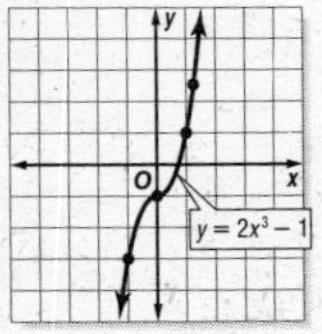

$y = 2x^3 - 1$

Exercises

Graph each function.

1. $y = x^2 + 2$

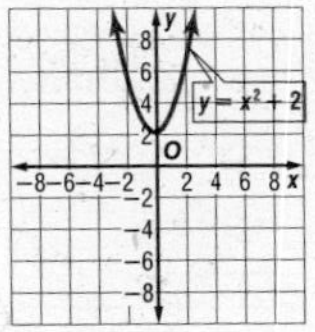

2. $y = x^3 + 2$

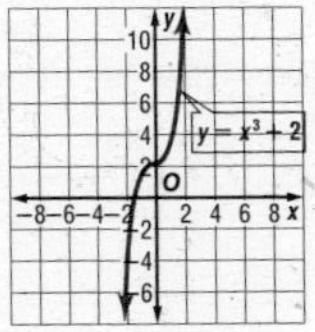

3. $y = -x^2 + 2$

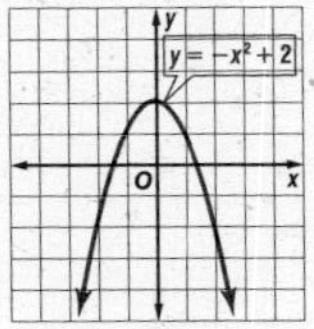

4. $y = -x^3 + 2$

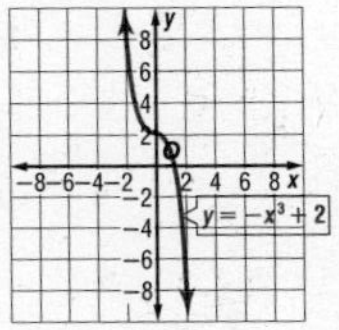

5. $y = x^2 - 2$

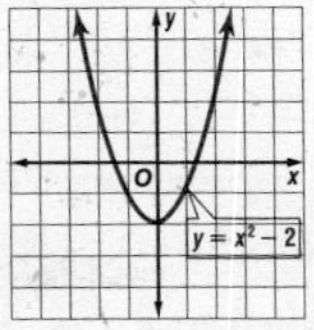

6. $y = x^3 - 2$

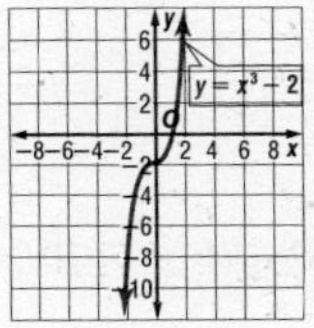

Page (Lesson Reading Guide)

NAME _____ DATE _____ PERIOD _____

13-6 Lesson Reading Guide

Graphing Quadratic and Cubic Functions

Get Ready for the Lesson

Read the introduction to Lesson 13-6 in your textbook. Write your answers below.

a. The volume of cube V equals the cube of the length of an edge a. Write a formula to represent the volume of a cube as a function of edge length. $V = a^3$

b. Graph the volume as a function of edge length. (*Hint:* Use values of a like 0, 0.5, 1, 1.5, 2, and so on.)

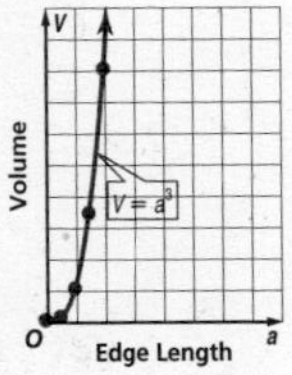

c. Would it be reasonable to use negative numbers for x values in this situation? **No; the side of a cube cannot have a negative length.**

Read the Lesson

1. Write a quadratic function. Explain what makes it a quadratic function and what its graph would look like. **Sample answer:** $y = 2x^2 + 5$; **This is a quadratic function because it has the form** $y = ax^2 + bx + c$, $a \neq 0$. **It is a parabola.**

2. Write a cubic function. Explain what makes it a cubic function and what its graph would look like. **Sample answer:** $y = 3x^3 + 2$; **This is a cubic function because it has the form** $y = ax^3 + bx^2 + cx$, $a \neq 0$. **It is similar in appearance to** $y = x^3$, **only shifted up two units and increasing more rapidly.**

Remember What You Learned

3. You have learned to graph quadratic and cubic functions. Make a list of the steps you use to graph the two functions.

Make a table of values.

Plot the ordered pairs.

Connect the points with a curve.

Answers (Lesson 13-6)

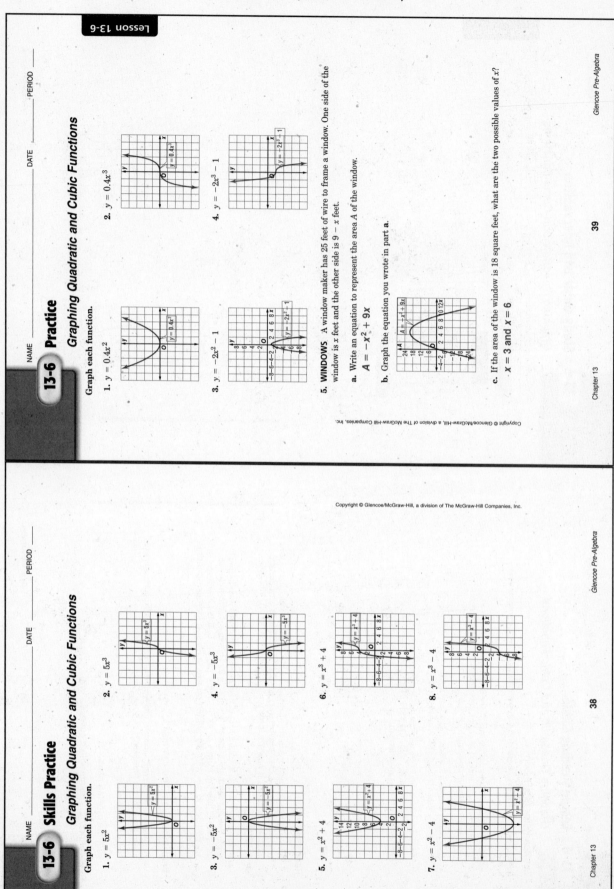

NAME _____ DATE _____ PERIOD _____

13-6 Practice

Graphing Quadratic and Cubic Functions

Graph each function.

1. $y = 0.4x^2$

2. $y = 0.4x^3$

3. $y = -2x^2 - 1$

4. $y = -2x^3 - 1$

5. **WINDOWS** A window maker has 25 feet of wire to frame a window. One side of the window is x feet and the other side is $9 - x$ feet.

   a. Write an equation to represent the area A of the window.

   $A = -x^2 + 9x$

   b. Graph the equation you wrote in part a.

   c. If the area of the window is 18 square feet, what are the two possible values of x?

   $x = 3$ and $x = 6$

Chapter 13   39   Glencoe Pre-Algebra

NAME _____ DATE _____ PERIOD _____

13-6 Skills Practice

Graphing Quadratic and Cubic Functions

Graph each function.

1. $y = 5x^2$

2. $y = 5x^3$

3. $y = -5x^2$

4. $y = -5x^3$

5. $y = x^2 + 4$

6. $y = x^3 + 4$

7. $y = x^2 - 4$

8. $y = x^3 - 4$

Chapter 13   38   Glencoe Pre-Algebra

Chapter 13

A18

Glencoe Pre-Algebra

Lesson 13-6

13-6 Enrichment

Translating Quadratic Graphs

When a figure is moved to a new position without undergoing any rotation, then the figure is said to have been **translated** to the new position.

The graph of a quadratic equation in the form $y = (x - b)^2 + c$ is a translation of the graph of $y = x^2$.

Start with a graph of $y = x^2$.

Slide to the right 4 units.

$$y = (x - 4)^2$$

Then slide up 3 units.

$$y = (x - 4)^2 + 3$$

The following equations are in the form $y = x^2 + c$. Graph each equation.

1. $y = x^2 + 1$

2. $y = x^2 + 2$

3. $y = x^2 - 2$

The following equations are in the form $y = (x - b)^2$. Graph each equation.

4. $y = (x - 1)^2$

5. $y = (x - 3)^2$

6. $y = (x + 2)^2$

13-6 Word Problem Practice

Graphing Quadratic and Cubic Functions

1. **RACING** Between the ages of 8 and 16, Houston native Erica Enders won 37 junior dragster races. The distance her car travels down the drag strip can be expressed by the equation $d = \frac{1}{2}at^2$, where a is the rate of acceleration and t is time. Suppose her car accelerates at a rate of 49.5 feet per second. Find the number of feet her car traveled after 7 seconds.
1212.75 feet

2. **PHYSICS** The top of the Leaning Tower of Pisa is 185 feet above the ground. Suppose an object is dropped from the top of the Leaning Tower of Pisa. The height h in feet of the object, after t seconds, is represented by the equation $h = 185 - 16t^2$. How far from the ground is it after 3 seconds?
41 ft

3. **VISTAS** The Texas State Capitol building is 311 feet tall. The formula $a = \frac{2}{3}d^2$ represents the number of miles d that a person can see from an altitude of a feet. Graph the function and use it to estimate how far you could see from the top of the Texas State Capitol.

Sample answer: about 20 miles (exact answer 21.6 miles)

4. **GEOMETRY** Write the function for the volume of a cone as a function of a radius r units if the height equals the radius. Then graph the function.
$$V = \frac{1}{3}\pi r^3$$

FIREWORKS For Exercises 5 and 6, use the following information.
The largest annual pyrotechnic display in North America is *Thunder over Louisville* held to kick off the Kentucky Derby Festival. The table shows the larger shell sizes and their corresponding velocities.

Shell Size (in.)	Initial Velocity (ft/sec)
8	235
10	263
12	287.5
24	393
36	481

Source: www.pyropage.net/physics.html

5. The equation $h = -16t^2 + 235t + 3$ represents the height h in feet of an 8-inch shell t seconds after it is launched from 3 feet with an initial velocity of 235 feet per second. Graph the equation.

6. How high is the shell after 5 seconds?
778 feet

Copyright © Glencoe/McGraw-Hill, a division of The McGraw-Hill Companies, Inc.

NAME _____ DATE _____ PERIOD _____

13-6 Spreadsheet Activity

Families of Quadratic Graphs

A *family of graphs* is a group of graphs that have at least one characteristic in common. You can use a spreadsheet to study the characteristics of families of quadratic graphs.

Example Graph the quadratics $y = x^2$, $y = 2x^2$, and $y = 4x^2$. What are the similarities and differences among the graphs?

Step 1 Use the Column A for the values of x and Columns B, C, and D for the values of y. Exponents are entered using the ^ symbol. For example, cell B2 contains the formula A2^2.

Step 2 To create a graph from the data, select the data in Columns A, B, C, and D and choose Chart from the Insert menu. Select an XY (Scatter) chart with a smooth line to show the graphs.

Quadratic.xls

	A	B	C	D
1	x	y=x^2	y=2x^2	y=4x^2
2	-5	25	50	100
3	-4	16	32	64
4	-3	9	18	36
5	-2	4	8	16
6	-1	1	2	4
7	0	0	0	0
8	1	1	2	4
9	2	4	8	16
10	3	9	18	36
11	4	16	32	64
12	5	25	50	100

Sheet 1 / Sheet 2 / Sheet 3

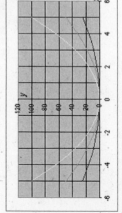

The graphs of all three functions pass through the point at (0, 0).

The graph of $y = x^2$ is wider than the graph of $y = 2x^2$. The graph of $y = 2x^2$ is wider than the graph of $y = 4x^2$.

Exercises

1. Make a conjecture about the graph of $y = \frac{1}{2}x^2$ as compared to the graphs above. Use the spreadsheet to graph $y = \frac{1}{2}x^2$ and verify your conjecture.

   It passes through (0, 0) and is wider than the graph of $y = x^2$.

2. Graph the quadratics $y = x^2$, $y = x^2 + 2$, and $y = x^2 - 3$. What are the similarities and differences among the graphs? **See students' graphs. The graphs are all the same shape, but the graph of $y = x^2$ passes through (0, 0), $y = x^2 + 2$ passes through (0, 2), and $y = x^2 - 3$ passes through (0, -3).**

Chapter 13 Assessment Answer Key

Quiz 1 (Lessons 13–1 and 13–2)
Page 45

1. ___yes; trinomial___

2. ___no___

3. ___2___

4. ___1___

5. ___binomial___

6. ___$6m + 11$___

7. ___$7x + 1$___

8. ___$10y + 3s$___

9. ___$10p^2 + 3p + 9$___

10. ___$-x^2y - xy$___

Quiz 2 (Lesson 13-3)
Page 45

1. ___$5y - 3$___

2. ___$3x + y$___

3. ___$2x^2 - 7x$___

4. ___$12x^2 - x - 7$___

5. ___$2x - 3$___

Quiz 3 (Lessons 13–4 and 13–5)
Page 46

1. ___$27a + 3a^2$___

2. ___$-6c^5 + 12c^3 - 42c$___

3. ___Nonlinear; the graph is not a straight line.___

4. ___Linear; the rate of change is constant.___

5. ___B___

Quiz 4 (Lesson 13-6)
Page 46

1.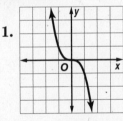

2.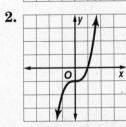

3.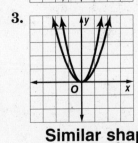

___Similar shape; $y = 2x^2$ is narrower.___

Mid-Chapter Test
Page 47

1. ___C___

2. ___H___

3. ___B___

4. ___F___

5. ___A___

6. ___H___

7. ___D___

8. ___yes; monomial___

9. ___no___

10. ___yes; trinomial___

11. ___$9x + 12$___

12. ___$b - 11$___

13. ___$4x + 3$___

14. ___$2a^2 - 7b + 6$___

Answers

Chapter 13 Assessment Answer Key

Vocabulary Test
Page 48

1. true

2. true

3. false; 5

4. false; cubic

5. false; trinomial

6. true

7. false; linear function

8. false; additive inverse

9. true

10. true

11. the sum of the exponents of its variables

12. the same as that of the term with the greatest degree

Form 1
Page 49

1. __A__

2. __G__

3. __C__

4. __H__

5. __B__

6. __H__

7. __A__

8. __J__

9. __B__

10. __H__

11. __A__

12. __J__

Page 50

13. __C__

14. __G__

15. __A__

16. __J__

17. __C__

18. __F__

19. __C__

20. __G__

B: __$8x - 2y - 8$__

Chapter 13 Assessment Answer Key

Form 2A
Page 51

Page 52

Form 2B
Page 53

Page 54

Form 2A — Page 51

1. C
2. F
3. C
4. F
5. B
6. H
7. A
8. J
9. B
10. G
11. D

Page 52

12. G
13. C
14. F
15. D
16. G
17. C
18. F
19. D
20. J

Sample answer:
B: $3x^2y^2 + 3xy$

Form 2B — Page 53

1. B
2. J
3. C
4. H
5. B
6. F
7. D
8. G
9. C
10. F
11. C

Page 54

12. G
13. C
14. F
15. D
16. G
17. A
18. F
19. C
20. H

Sample answer:
B: $x^2y^3 + 3x^2 + 5$

Answers

Chapter 13 Assessment Answer Key

Form 2C
Page 55

1. **yes; trinomial**

2. **yes; monomial**

3. $4y + 2x + 2xy$

4. 2

5. $5x + 7$

6. $4y + 4$

7. $5a^2 - 3a + 2b^2$

8. $3t^2 - 15s^2$

9. $5x^2 + 3x - 2$

10. $8x + 6$

11. 5

12. **13 cm by 10 cm**

13. $12x + 3$

14. $-5b^2 - 2b$

15. $3y^2 + 6y$

16. $12a^2 + 36a$

17. $-16c^2 + 4c$

18. $k^3m - 2km$

Page 56

19. **tennis, 27 ft by 78 ft; badminton, 17 ft by 44 ft**

20. **Nonlinear; the graph is not a straight line.**

21. **Linear; the rate of change is constant.**

22. **Nonlinear; the equation cannot be written as $y = mx + b$.**

23.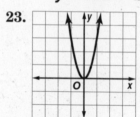

24.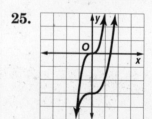

25.

Yes; every value of x is paired with a unique value of y.

Sample answer:
B: $(5x^2 + 9x - 3) - (3x^2 + 8x - 7)$

Chapter 13 Assessment Answer Key

Form 2D
Page 57

Page 58

1. _____no_____

2. _yes; trinomial_

3. $4y + 2x + 2xy$

4. _____2_____

5. _____$8x + 5$_____

6. _____$5y + 4$_____

7. $4a^2 - 2a + 2b^2$

8. $3t^2 - 17s^2$

9. $3x^2 + 6x - 4$

10. _____$8x - 2$_____

11. _____5_____

12. _12 cm by 7 cm_

13. _____$20x - 8$_____

14. _____$-6b^2 - b$_____

15. _____$2y^2 + 7y$_____

16. _____$10a^2 + 35a$_____

17. _____$-15c^2 + 6c$_____

18. _____$k^4m + 4km$_____

19. singles, 27 ft by 78 ft; doubles, 36 ft by 78 ft

20. Linear; the graph is a straight line.

21. Nonlinear; the rate of change is not constant.

22. Linear; the equation is in the form $y = mx + b$.

23.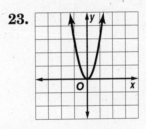

24.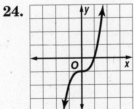

25.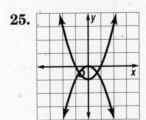

Yes; every value of x is paired with a unique value of y.

B: $(8x^3 - 36x^2 + 16x)cm^2$

Answers

Chapter 13 Assessment Answer Key

Form 3
Page 59

1. _____ no _____

2. _ yes; trinomial _

3. _ Sometimes; $x^2 + 3$ has degree 2 but $x^3 + 3$ has degree 3. _

4. _ Always; a trinomial is a polynomial with 3 terms. _

5. _ $11x - 2$ _

6. _ $5k - 2$ _

7. _ $7z^2 + 5zw + w^2$ _

8. _ $2x^2 - xy - 2y^2$ _

9. _ $-7x^2 + 5x - 2$ _

10. _ $6b - 4a$; 26 _

11. _ $3a^2 + 3b^2 - 1$; 38 _

12. _ $3a + 4b + 5c$; 31 _

13. _ $x^2 - 7x$ _

14. _ $6y^3 - 12y$ _

15. _ $-r^3s - 5rs$ _

16. _ $-12x^2 + 8x - 44$ _

17. _ $-14m + 8m^2 - 6m^3$ _

18. _ $5b^4 + 45b^2 - 20b$ _

19. _____ 3 _____

Page 60

20. _ Linear; the rate of change is constant. _

21. _ Nonlinear; the graph is a curve. _

22. _ Nonlinear; the equation cannot be written as $y = mx + b$. _

23.

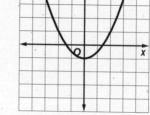

24.

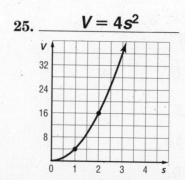

25. _ $V = 4s^2$ _

B: _ 77 ft by 86 ft _

Chapter 13 Assessment Answer Key

Page 61, Extended-Response Test
Scoring Rubric

Score	General Description	Specific Criteria
4	**Superior** A correct solution that is supported by well-developed, accurate explanations	• Shows thorough understanding of the concepts of *identifying, classifying, and finding the degree of a polynomial, adding and subtracting polynomials, determining whether a function is linear or nonlinear,* and *graphing cubic functions.* • Uses appropriate strategies to solve problems. • Computations are correct. • Written explanations are exemplary. • Graphs are accurate and appropriate. • Goes beyond requirements of some or all problems.
3	**Satisfactory** A generally correct solution, but may contain minor flaws in reasoning or computation	• Shows an understanding of the concepts of *identifying, classifying, and finding the degree of a polynomial, adding and subtracting polynomials, determining whether a function is linear or nonlinear,* and *graphing cubic functions.* • Uses appropriate strategies to solve problems. • Computations are mostly correct. • Written explanations are effective. • Graphs are mostly accurate and appropriate. • Satisfies all requirements of problems.
2	**Nearly Satisfactory** A partially correct interpretation and/or solution to the problem	• Shows an understanding of most of the concepts of *identifying, classifying, and finding the degree of a polynomial, adding and subtracting polynomials, determining whether a function is linear or nonlinear,* and *graphing cubic functions.* • May not use appropriate strategies to solve problems. • Computations are mostly correct. • Written explanations are satisfactory. • Graphs are mostly accurate. • Satisfies the requirements of most of the problems.
1	**Nearly Unsatisfactory** A correct solution with no supporting evidence or explanation	• Final computation is correct. • No written explanations or work is shown to substantiate the final computation. • Graphs may be accurate but lack detail or explanation. • Satisfies minimal requirements of some of the problems.
0	**Unsatisfactory** An incorrect solution indicating no mathematical understanding of the concept or task, or no solution is given	• Shows little or no understanding of most of the concepts of *identifying, classifying, and finding the degree of a polynomial, adding and subtracting polynomials, determining whether a function is linear or nonlinear,* and *graphing cubic functions.* • Does not use appropriate strategies to solve problems. • Computations are incorrect. • Written explanations are unsatisfactory. • Graphs are inaccurate or inappropriate. • Does not satisfy requirements of problems. • No answer may be given.

Chapter 13 Assessment Answer Key

Page 61, Extended-Response Test
Sample Answers

In addition to the scoring rubric found on page A27, the following sample answers may be used as guidance in evaluating open-ended assessment items.

1a.

Sample Polynomial	Number of Terms	Type of Polynomial	Degree of Polynomial
$\frac{3}{5}x^4$	1	monomial	4
$3r^3 - r^2$	2	binomial	3
$a^2 + 2ab + b^2$	3	trinomial	2
$x^4y^3 + 4x^3y - 15xy^2$	3	trinomial	7

1b. Sample answer: $x^3 + x^2 + 1$

1c. Sample answer: xyz

1d. $x^3 + x^2 + 1$ has 3 terms that contain different powers of x, but xyz is a product of 3 variables. xyz is only one term.

2a. $3x^2 + 2x - 4$

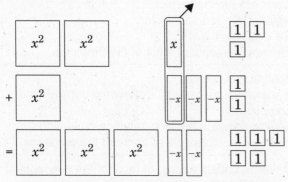

2b.
$$2x^2 + x + 3$$
$$\underline{x^2 - 3x + 2}$$
$$3x^2 - 2x + 5$$

Remove the zero pair and group like pairs.

2c.
$$3x^2 + 3x + 5$$
$$\underline{-x^2 + 4x + 2}$$
$$2x^2 - x + 3$$

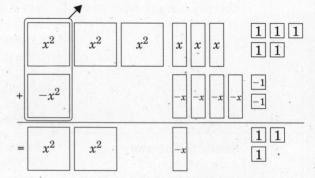

3a.

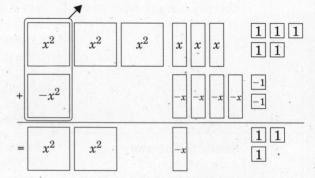

3b.

3c. Nonlinear; the graph is a curve.

3d. $y = x^3 + 1$

Chapter 13 Assessment Answer Key

Standardized Test Practice

Page 62   **Page 63**

9. Ⓐ ● Ⓒ Ⓓ

1. Ⓐ Ⓑ ● Ⓓ

10. Ⓕ Ⓖ ● Ⓙ

2. ● Ⓖ Ⓗ Ⓙ

11. Ⓐ Ⓑ Ⓒ ●

12. Ⓕ Ⓖ ● Ⓙ

3. Ⓐ ● Ⓒ Ⓓ

13. Ⓐ ● Ⓒ Ⓓ

4. Ⓕ Ⓖ ● Ⓙ

14. Ⓕ Ⓖ ● Ⓙ

15. Ⓐ ● Ⓒ Ⓓ

16. Ⓕ ● Ⓗ Ⓙ

5. Ⓐ Ⓑ ● Ⓓ

17.

		1	2	.	2	
0	0	0	0		0	0
1	1	●	1		1	1
2	2	2	●		●	2
3	3	3	3		3	3
4	4	4	4		4	4
5	5	5	5		5	5
6	6	6	6		6	6
7	7	7	7		7	7
8	8	8	8		8	8
9	9	9	9		9	9

6. Ⓕ Ⓖ ● Ⓙ

7. Ⓐ Ⓑ ● Ⓓ

18.

			3	.		
0	0	0	0		0	0
1	1	1	1		1	1
2	2	2	2		2	2
3	3	3	●		3	3
4	4	4	4		4	4
5	5	5	5		5	5
6	6	6	6		6	6
7	7	7	7		7	7
8	8	8	8		8	8
9	9	9	9		9	9

8. ● Ⓖ Ⓗ Ⓙ

Chapter 13 Assessment Answer Key

Standardized Test Practice

Page 64

19. $1:7; 13$

20. $4r^2$; yes

21. 7

22. 7

23. 2.85×10^9

24. -1

25. $y = 3x + 7$

26. $20; 20°, 142°$

27. 384.8 cm^2

28. 15 in.

29. $15x^2 - 9x$

30a. 27

30b. 18

30c. 36

Chapter 13 Assessment Answer Key

1. _____65_____

2. _____50–59_____

3. _____49_____

4.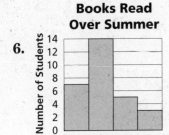
   20 30 40 50 60 70

5. _____20_____

6.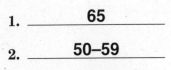

Books Read Over Summer

7. _____22_____

8. Graph B; the vertical scale on graph B starts at 60 and has intervals of 10. This makes the increase in stock price appear to be dramatic.

9. _____12_____

10. _____$\frac{3}{8}$_____

11. permutation; 362,880

12. combination; 495

13. _____$\frac{5}{12}$_____

14. _____$\frac{1}{15}$_____

15. _____$\frac{5}{8}$_____

16. yes; binomial

17. _____3_____

18. $6a^2 + ab + b$

19. $2x^2 - 2x - 10$

20. $3x + 2y$ cm

21. $3x^2 - x$

22. $-40a + 8a^2$

23. $8x - 4y$

24. nonlinear; the equation cannot be written as $y = mx + b$.

25.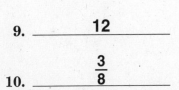